CLIVE THE CAT CHIMES IN

MUSINGS ON MY HUMANS, FOOD, AND GOD

LORAL PEPOON

with CLIVE

Selah Press
PUBLISHING

Clive the Cat Chimes In: Musings on My Humans, Food, and God
© 2023 by Loral Pepoon (loralpepoon.com)

Editor: Venessa Knizley, venessa.knizley@gmail.com
Cover Design: Lisa Thompson, BZ Studio
Publisher: Selah Press Publishing, selah-press.com
Headshot Photography: Jenni McCadams
Cat Photography: Loral and Seth Pepoon, loralpepoon.com

ISBNs: Paperback 978-1-953211-34-7; Hardcover: 978-1-953211-33-0; eBook: 978-1-953211-35-4

DEDICATION

To my parents and grandparents—
Any success I've had in my editorial career and
in fulfilling my dreams of becoming an author
has been made possible because each of you watered
the seeds of my God-given creativity.

Thank you for your love,
hard work, and financial sacrifice,
which made my private school education
and master's degree possible.

May the Lord multiply your collective gifts to me so that
I can bless my own bonus children and grandchildren.

All my love,
Loral

CONTENTS

Me as an adorable kitten, with my whole life ahead of me, dreaming as I look upward...

1
THE SAME...
ONLY DIFFERENT

Hi! I'm Clive. Welcome to my musings! I know you have great taste because you were likely drawn to this book because of my exceedingly handsome cover shot. And now to the left, you get to see me as a young, adorable lad. I can almost hear you saying, "aww..." just like the humans do when they visit me in person and see this photograph on the fridge.

I chose this picture for my first musing because it demonstrates that I haven't changed that much over time...

- I'm still uber good looking.

- I still have striking markings and an interesting fur pattern.

- I still look up in the same dreamy, pensive manner.

My upward gaze is my favorite thing about both my cover shot and my kitten picture. In various musings that follow, I will tell you more about the thoughts behind this pose, during which I look up at my humans, my foodie bag, or toward God, but first, let me start out with some other fundamentals...

I like to write...My first human must have expected I would because she named me after C.S. Lewis (spelled out Clive Staples), the prolific author of more than 30 books, including the Narnia Series and many others. C.S. Lewis was also nicknamed Jack—and so am I.

In this first musing, I thought it would be appropriate to quote my namesake:

"Isn't it funny how day by day nothing changes, but when you look back, everything is different..."[1]

I've already pointed out what hasn't changed since I was a kitten. So, allow me to move on to what's different. As you can see, I was a fraction of my size as a kitten that I am today. Although I was precious as a kitten, today I say, "The more of me, the better."

Not only has my size changed, but my life circumstances are different as well.

- **I had a different human as a kitten than I do now.** My current mommy (Loral) rented a room in my first human's (Carole's) house. At the time, these two special ladies lived with another wonderful lady, who I still call Aunt Joanie. Although Carole loved me dearly, I was under her feet too much for her comfort. After Carole had ankle surgery, she began praying for someone special to adopt me.

- **I was blessed to find a human who wanted to be home all day just to be around me!** Immediately after Loral moved in with these two ladies, she fell in love with me. She loved me so much that she began working from home— before that was common. She claimed she started working from home because she moved away from her workplace, but I know that I was the real reason she continued to work from home. Carole was delighted that I was bonding with this new person in her house, and she had an inkling that her prayers for me to be adopted were about to be answered…

- **My mommy officially became my mommy when she married my daddy!** One year after Loral moved into the home with the two other ladies, she met my daddy. When Daddy popped the question 100 days later, he immediately said, "And we can adopt Jack." I know Mommy would have married Daddy without that part of the offer, but I know me being part of the deal was the icing on the proverbial cake.

Despite all these changes early in our relationship, Mommy—like me—is at her core, still the same as she was when we first met. She was and is a woman who loves Jesus and others who are dear to her. After Jesus and Daddy, she loves me most of all.

She loves me so much that she has typed MANY of my words. I started sharing my wisdom with her a few years before dictation software was efficient like it is now. I have always been pretty amazing, but I haven't yet mastered the paws on the keyboard thing.

I have, however, mastered lying on her keyboard, especially when she has a deadline—and getting garbly-gook onto her screen. I'll demonstrate that now…

(saekajehrkrfafalfjalfalsfjlfajelfakaoifasffkiuRHWIUHAHAWRHKUFAHUAHR.)

Instead of garbly-gook, with Mommy's help, I hope you find my musings sometimes entertaining, sometimes insightful, and sometimes practical. I've found that you humans need all the help you can get—so I offer much advice. If you could be around me, you'd get this help in the form of various meowing tones that Mommy would translate. I assure you—I am quite vocal!

I'd rather meet you in person so that you could experience how amazing I am, but since I can't meet all of you, my musings will have to do!

I will not only communicate my thoughts about whatever I fancy, but also, I will invite you to think about your life in a section called "What About You?" I included that part because Mommy says conversations are best and that considering the needs of others is, well, considerate.

If you're a journaling type, you might even want to record any thoughts or ideas sparked by my words. You never know—your reflections could turn into a book just like mine have!

That's enough about you—for a bit longer, let's get back to my favorite subject—me!

Although I hope you enjoy my musings, I know that you may find my words irrelevant to your life. I'm okay with that. This is my book, so I've written whatever I've wanted to! I didn't do a marketing study to see what cat owners want, or any other such fiddle-faddle…My cat-ness ensures I know best what I want to do!

Still, I invite you to grab a cup of tea (or coffee for you typical American types), to settle into your favorite chair, and to get ready to laugh from my humor and to grow from my insights.

And if you enjoy this book, share it on your socials and write a review on Amazon… After all, a cat's got to eat!

Meow for now,

Clive

Sitting in my favorite British pose,
showing off my portly belly.

2

LIVING UP TO MY NAME

"What's in a name?" Romeo asks in Shakespeare's most famous love story, Romeo and Juliet. I relate to Romeo because I'm a 23-pound-hunk-of-feline LOVE! I direct my love to my humans and foodie, but for now, let me get back to telling you about my name.

I wanted to use my formal name, Clive, for my book because Clive the Cat just has a nicer, more interesting ring to it than Jack the Cat does. Besides, what good writer doesn't love alliteration—that's the repetition of the "c"s for those of you who didn't retain the literary devices taught in English class. 🐾

The name Clive sounds more British, and Jack sounds more American—and mundane. I've noticed humans are more drawn to things that sound exotic and foreign. So, I'm hoping that as you and others read this book, you will almost be able to hear my British accent… Who knows, I may even record an audio book someday!

To live up to my British name, I often sit up in a very civilized manner, showing off my portly stomach, like you see in the photo to the left. All that's missing in my British look is a top hat and round reading spectacles.

Maybe I really am British. I'm extremely fond of sticking my nose in Mommy's teacup. I can't help myself—it smells delightful. I don't love the taste of tea quite as much as the smell, though. Mommy (or should I call her Mum) keeps her tea a smidgen too hot for me to drink.

Names not only invoke the nationality of origin of a name, but Mommy says that talking about naming things reminds her of a nugget of wisdom from God, who says in His book (the Bible):

> If you decree something, it will stand; light will shine on your ways
> (Job 22:28, CEB).

Mommy says that one way people decree something is to speak it out.

So, I declare that I will become a prolific author like my British namesake, Clive Staples (C.S.) Lewis. Lewis' Website says that he was "one of the intellectual giants of the twentieth century and arguably one of the most influential writers of his day."[2] His Web site goes on to say his Narnia series has sold more than 100 million copies.[3]

If I sold 1/100th as many books as my namesake, my humans would be able to pursue their passions for the rest of their lives without being as concerned about money. As you can probably already tell, my humans are wonderful, so I want them to live a fulfilled life without stress—just like I do!

Another thing I would do if I sold loads of books is that I would be charitable to those outside my family like C.S. Lewis was. I would give money to make sure my local feline friends have plenty of yummy foodie. I LOVE MY FOODIE! Maybe then more of them could become bigger hunks-of-feline love—like me!

To be sure, other cats will never be exactly like me—because I'm one of a kind!

However, if more cats had more foodie, they would be happier, and that could make them over-the-top friendly, also like me. We could then overtake the canines as the preferred pet for humans!

And, I might add, I think we cats should be the preferred pet for you humans because felines are so much easier to take care of than crazy canines! You humans can leave us for a few days (with extra food and water). We can walk ourselves, and we don't require you to go outside when it's freezing or scalding hot just so we can get rid of our waste! We can also manage getting into our own "box," thank you very much!

That's enough for this musing about my name and my desire to live up to my namesake to benefit my humans and other felines…It's time to bring you into the conversation…

What About You?
Do you know if you were named for anyone? Have you ever looked up your name's meaning? If you find attributes that you like in your name's meaning, I encourage

you to embrace them as your own. If you would like to be like these traits but that seems difficult, you might consider asking God for help. In case you didn't know, God invites you to ask Him for help—and He gives help with His name. He says: "If you ask anything in my name, I will do it" (John 14:14, ESV).

Are there any other qualities you want others to think about when they hear your name? Is there one step you could take today to bring that quality into your life? Got it? Great! How about getting started before you forget! At the very least pause here to write down your idea. My words will be waiting for you when you get back…

I will say before I sign off that I'm rooting for you—well, I'm not jumping up and down because I'm still sitting in my favorite lazy position on the couch, but I'm rooting for you in spirit!

Meow for now,

Clive

Me licking Daddy's finger, asking
him to get my gunk out...

3
GETTING THE GUNK OUT

Now that I've introduced you to some of the traits of my wonderful personality and told you about my name, I thought it would be appropriate for the next musing to begin with how I start my day.

What I'm going to share next may not seem like what an aspiring feline celebrity would want to share first, but I've never been one to hold back, so here it goes…

I've got gunk. This icky, crusty brown matter in the corner of my eyes acts like glue, making it harder for me to wake up. Therefore, the first part of my morning routine is letting one of my humans clean the gunk out of my eyes. I don't want to be delayed in getting to my all-important morning activities, which I'll describe more in a bit… First, though, I need to disclose some of my "emotional gunk." Mommy says physical gunk can be related to psychological baggage.

I initially resisted help getting my gunk out because I didn't know better. When Mommy first started trying to get my gunk out, I would squirm and try to get away. That was a futile effort—Mommy never let me go. Before Mommy started to clean my eyes, I didn't know life without the gunk. I guess I just accepted gunky eyes as part of my limitations of being feline—kind of like how I have to rely on these tall creatures to feed me. But I've learned that…

I'm better off without my "gunk." After a few weeks of Mommy or Daddy forcing me to be still during the de-gunking process, I learned to not fight it. If I don't sit still, Mommy could poke me in the eye with her longer colored nails—and that could hurt! Daddy's fingers are a little big in comparison to my paw, so I don't want to fight him either. I discovered that once one of them gets my gunk out, it is then easier for me to use my own paws to finish washing the rest of my face and to give my hunk-of-feline-body a bath.

Without gunk, not only can I finish my self-grooming, but also, I can see more clearly to run faster to my morning bowl of foodie. I LOVE MY FOODIE! Once I'm nourished, I have the energy to jump up onto my humans laps for plenty of head petting and purring for my favorite activity ever: couch time. I'll tell you more about that later, but it's relaxing and invigorating, as well as educational and relational. Couch time is not the point of this musing, and I don't want to get "gunked" up with a tangent…(See how I did that? I think I'm becoming more of a genius writer every day!)

So, without further delay—back to the real gunk…

Not only do I not resist my humans cleaning my eyes when I first wake up, now, I let them know that I WANT their help getting my gunk out by licking their fingers.

Asking for help de-gunking was one of the best lessons I ever learned!! Once I experienced clearer vision, a gunk-free life, and the freedom said gunk-free living gives me, I didn't want to go back to being gunked up. So I'll keep asking for help—every day!

As I interact with both humans and felines, I have seen that sometimes we independent creatures think that asking for help makes us look weak. I suggest we all throw our pride (whether human or feline in nature) to the curb and request assistance. You humans may want to use a different method than licking fingers, though! Now that I have less gunk, I can ask…

What About You?
What gunk are you living with? Who can you ask for help to get your gunk out? Is there someone you already know who may be ready to assist? Would it be wise for you to call a personal trainer, a doctor, a house cleaner—or perhaps a counselor or pastor for the emotional gunk?

Getting help may be just what you need. If you feel embarrassment or shame about asking for help, you may also want to ask God to help you deal with those feelings. Mommy says these pesky emotions are just more gunk in our own minds. God is a master at getting mind gunk out—and He loves you!

Because it's so important, I'll reiterate—Don't let shame stop you from asking for help! If I can let someone whose 10 times taller and bigger than me stick a much bigger paw with colored claws near my eye, and actually like it, surely, you can ask for help too.

I encourage you to believe God when He says:

> Let us then fearlessly *and* confidently *and* boldly draw near to the throne of grace (the throne of God's unmerited favor to us sinners), that we may receive mercy [for our failures] and find grace to help in good time for every need [appropriate help and well-timed help, coming just when we need it] (Hebrews 4:16, AMPC).

With God or someone else's help, you may be able to do what you want with more energy and ease! Then you, too, will enjoy the things in life that you treasure the most even more.

That musing was pretty philosophical. I think I need more foodie after all this thinking! I LOVE MY FOODIE!

Meow for now,

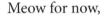

Clive

4

I'm Everywhere They Are

I hear my humans say often that I am more like a dog than a cat. I think they may be right because I follow them everywhere like a dog would. I can't help it! I love being with my mommy and daddy—well, I like to sleep too. I like to eat even more than anything, and if I'm honest, that was my first motivation to be wherever my humans are (don't tell Mommy and Daddy I said that—I don't want to hurt their feelings). My love for my humans, however, is still a formidable competitor to my eating in determining my location at any given time. Regardless of my motivation, whenever I am awake, I'm usually wherever my humans are.

I go to the productive places. My mommy's laptop is most often on her lap when she is home because she has much to do so that she can both write down everything I say and finish her other writing and editing work. I usually jump right between her lap and her hands. If she doesn't stop to play with me, I push the buttons on the keyboard and type for myself—then she has a LOT more editing to do because she will have to erase what I typed! I finally got her to focus on MY book—and I think we make a great team. 🐾

I go to the yummy places. If my parents are eating, I smell the food, and I go sit on the floor beside the dining room table. At some point not too long into their meal, I put my front paws on the side of one of my parent's chairs. If there is space between the table and one of my human's torsos, I'll jump in a lap. They love me, and they enjoy me being with them. I know that if I am too aggressive—if I jump onto the table—I will get a spanking. It's a much better strategy for me to play cute and to politely share my desire for some of their foodie with a gentle meow. With these tactics, they usually share a bite of something yummy with me on a plate when they are done. But if I try to get foodie by myself from the table, I usually don't get anything—except for a running start down the hall to try to escape punishment from Daddy!

I go to the scary places. Sometimes my parents eat outside on the patio. It is scary and loud because of the large moving objects around us. My humans call them cars and trucks. I call them monsters. There are even louder monsters in the sky because we live near an airport. I gently tiptoe outside with my back curled, ready to recoil if necessary. I stay hidden under one of my human's chairs, but it's worth being scared to be near my humans!

I go to the stinky places. I even follow my parents to the bathroom, where I sit on Mommy or Daddy's feet. They try to close the door most of the way to keep me out, but it doesn't shut all the way, so I bust in. That's how I got another nickname: Busting-in Buddy! If my parents close any door in our house, and my busting in with my burley physique doesn't work, I howl until whoever is inside that door comes to let me in. There are no closed doors for this cat!

I go to the loving places. I go to the couch where my parents sit and snuggle, and I wedge myself between them. If they are laying down watching a movie, I get to jump up on both their laps and watch it with them.

I'm kind of like Big Daddy—going everywhere my humans are! So, Big Daddy is one way my humans and I refer to God. Mommy and Daddy were always calling God "Daddy," and I was always listening to them talk about God, I thought, *God sounds like my daddy.* And they also always talk about how Big God is, so I started calling Him Big Daddy—and it stuck! We actually all have a bunch of names for God (and each other), but for simplicity's sake, in this book, when I talk about Him, I'll either use Big Daddy or God.

Anyway, just like my humans can't get away from me, you humans can't away from Big Daddy. He loves and pursues humans wherever they are. Mommy loves that Big Daddy pursues her so intently with the words and images that He shows her through His Word. She is so grateful that Jesus came to be with people on Earth (where they were), so that humans could be reconciled to a Holy God. Oh, how Big Daddy loves and wants to be with all those He created! I understand maybe a small sliver of Big Daddy's mind, because I want to be with His creatures that I know best—my humans—all the time too!

What About You?

Do you occasionally show people you love them with dog-like enthusiasm like I do? I suggest you make it a point to be obvious about your feelings of affection. Everyone wants to be loved! Just like when I went to the scary places, you may have to go outside of your comfort zone to be with your people.

Would you like a deeper spiritual journey? If so, I encourage you to read Big Daddy's book (the Bible). You may also want to ask Big Daddy to show Himself to you. Mommy and Daddy say He is everywhere. And I believe them. I am like Big Daddy, who created me because I'm also everywhere my people are.

Meow for now,

Clive

Climbing up to the next level to be closer to my humans getting ready in the bathroom.

5

STEPPING UP TO THE NEXT LEVEL

Morning get-ready time—When my parents are getting ready each morning in the bathroom, I sit by their feet. If they are looking in the mirror, and they don't pet me, I jump to the next level: the toilet seat. Even if the lid is up, I'm skilled at not landing in the bowl but straddling it instead! We felines were given the ability to balance on the bowl, because any cat will tell you that we like to drink water from the toilet better than from a cat dish.

If my humans still don't pet me when I'm on the toilet bowl rim, I go up another partial level. I rest my front legs and paws on the counter.

I love getting my paws on the counter where Daddy may be shaving or where Mommy may be putting her make up on. I will get in trouble if I get all the way up there, because I will be in the way or knock stuff onto the floor. But, just like mealtime, when I'm at the kitchen table, I go as far as I can in the bathroom without getting in trouble.

I push my limits. Although my social, outgoing personality makes me different from my fellow feline friends, in this instance, of getting as high up as possible, I am 100% cat. Do a search of the funniest cat videos online, and you will always find a cat jumping up onto something and falling off. We aren't scared of trying to get higher and falling. We usually land on our feet.

Speaking of falling, I'm perplexed…

Humans are so much bigger, with a more sophisticated brain than we felines have. So why, I wonder, are humans so fearful of stepping up to the next level? I do know that they aren't always as prone to land on their feet as we are.

You may miss the step and fall. So what?

Mommy says that Big Daddy (God) has made humans resilient. He has enabled them to get back up again. Humans are fortunate because Big Daddy also shares lessons with them when they fall. Us cats don't tend to learn quite as easily. Have you ever seen cats resist a laser light, even if they just bonked their bodies on a wall trying to catch the light? I rest my case.

If humans are wise, they will listen and heed Big Daddy's lessons.

Perhaps you are discouraged or gun shy because in the past you fell and had a hard time getting back on your feet. Perhaps you were going too fast, or it wasn't the right time to step up. That's okay. Big Daddy is all about giving you second, third, fourth, etc. chances. He will show you what to do and how to get there when He thinks it's time for you to jump to the next level.

Perhaps when you fell before, you needed someone to hold your hand as you stepped up, and you tried to do it alone instead. That's okay. At the right time, Big Daddy will provide you with someone else to help or to give you a greater ability than you had before to step out on your own.

You may look foolish when you fall. So what?

Are there any humans who haven't embarrassed themselves at one time or another? I'm waiting for you to come up with an answer other than no…But I know you can't. Mommy says it's better to try and be wrong than to never try at all. And, if some humans don't reach out but only laugh at you rather than helping you, those aren't the people you want in your life anyway. Some people will see you and help you. Those people are the compassionate, encouraging types of friends you want. And if a fall helps you find at least one of these people—or if that fall deepens your relationship with the person who helped you—something good would have come out of the fall.

You may be scared. So what?

If you are too scared to try stepping up to the next level, you will never know if you would've succeeded. Have you thought about what might happen if you were to succeed? Aren't you the least bit curious? Wouldn't you rather know if you could succeed than to always wonder and not try?

Mommy says if Big Daddy is calling you to take the next step, you will know it. And if He is calling you to step up to a new level, He will equip you to take that step. Ask

Him to help you to have courage to press through any fear and to watch him open up a whole new level of blessing. This morning Mommy was looking in the Bible for inspiration to help her get over some fears about work, and here is what she found and read to me:

> "But you, take courage! Do not let your hands be weak, for your work shall be rewarded" (2 Chronicles 15:7, ESV).

I hope this nugget inspires you like it does my mommy!

What About You?

What About You? What are your goals? How can you get to the next level? Does it require a balancing act? What incremental steps are in front of you that you can start with now? If we all step up one level at a time, could you imagine all that would be accomplished?

I'll end this message with a challenge: Don't be a scaredy-cat. Increase your cat-like curiosity and rely on your resilience to help you get back up—even if you fall. I know you can keep going and that you WILL keep stepping up to the next level! With God as your guide, new levels await! As the Bible says, "Nothing is impossible for God" (Luke 1:37, CEV)!

Meow for now,

Clive

Chest time with Daddy!

6

GUYS NIGHT IN

Experiencing an unusual weekend. One Friday evening, I began to notice something strange. Mommy wasn't home. She and Daddy are usually together.

Daddy was working on his blog, *Hiking with Your Honey*. He sat in his normal writing spot at the table, and I sat with him for a while in peace next to his feet. But then we went out onto the patio, which you may remember is one of my "scary places." For some reason, though, Daddy likes to go to the patio to take a break and think. Tonight, I was brave, and I went outside with him. It also helped that when it's dark, the scary mechanical birds that my humans call airplanes don't seem to fly overhead as much.

Every time Daddy got up to go inside, I expected him to go to the door and that Mommy would walk in.

But she didn't.

I began to get stressed.

Daddy did his best to comfort me. He fed me and scratched my head. The petting eased my pain a little, and I calmed down because it was time to go to bed. The next day, though, Daddy didn't engage in the normal routine of having our "couch time" right away. He had a morning appointment and more to do that Saturday than his ongoing technological and mechanical tasks.

Crying out for a familiar, comforting activity. I kept meowing at Daddy, because it had been more than 12 hours since I had seen Mommy, and I was missing her. But I was also meowing because I could tell my Daddy wasn't himself either. Finally, in an effort to comfort me, Daddy did something that comforted us both.

He sat down for "couch time." He got out my favorite blanket and our devotional books, and I ran up and jumped on His lap, like I always do. He began to read and pray like he and Mommy and I normally do each morning.

Finding peace. I think I was comforted by routine being reestablished, and Daddy was comforted by Big Daddy (God). Daddy told me that Big Daddy's power not only enables people to get tasks done, but that also His Spirit enables people to find the best direction for the day. I know Daddy was comforted because he relaxed, realizing he doesn't have to do everything himself.

A few hours later, Mommy came home. I was so excited to see her. I ran to her when the door opened, and Daddy picked me up so we could all be together in a hug. My purring motor roared with delight—and all was well.

Understanding that the discomfort had a purpose. It turns out, Mommy was at a women's conference at church. She loves her boys at home, but every once in a while, she needs extended fellowship and teaching with just the ladies. She came home tired from the deep teaching but with a satisfied soul. When she arose the next morning, she was refreshed and happy. We had our normal "couch time" once again—and all was back to normal.

What About You?

If your routine changes and discomfort ensues, what comforting activity could help divert your mind from your unusual circumstances? Who might you call or turn to for a listening ear for support as you adjust?

Have you ever noticed that disruptions to your routine make you have an appreciation for everyday activities once they are re-established? Perhaps you could consider thanking Big Daddy for the people that you love and for the everyday activities. As you appreciate the simple things and the everyday moments, your heightened gratitude may help you navigate life's challenges.

So, what simple, everyday things do you appreciate? A bath? A bed? Where you live? Sunshine? Yummy foodie? Waking up today?

> This *is* the day the Lord has made. We will rejoice and be glad in it (Psalm 118:24, NKJV).

Meow for now,

Clive

In one of my favorite places—Daddy's lap!

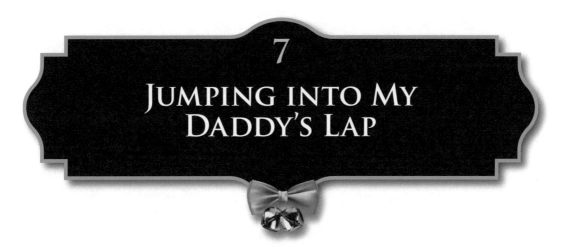

7
Jumping into My Daddy's Lap

I am howling this morning because my routine isn't exactly right. Mommy is up (typing these words for me), but Daddy isn't. When I can't see both of my parents, I get upset. I long for the comfort of both of them to be on the couch with me.

Despite my loudest howls, Daddy's Saturday slumber isn't broken. He finally relents and gets up after one of his friends calls, and they have a chance to talk.

Meanwhile, Mommy is trying to comfort me—to no avail. I need to see Daddy. I need to see him up and about, where I know that he is watching and caring for me.

The moment Daddy gets to the couch, I settle in on his lap, and I am comforted. After a few minutes, I am soothed enough to leave his lap and go rest on my own. I choose not to go too far—I lie down on Daddy's shoes. I can sleep peacefully there for quite some time. On that particular day, I was awakened by a cell phone ring. I was still laying there, but I had to look around and process what to do next. To deal with this new challenge, I needed more of Daddy.

Whenever I need more of Daddy, the best place I find comfort is on Daddy's lap. I look up at Him and jump onto his thighs once again. It doesn't matter what else Daddy is doing—I know my Daddy will stop everything to comfort me. And, once again, my genius-ness shines through! Daddy did stop everything to comfort me! I LOVE MY DADDY!

Similarly, God, as my humans' Heavenly Father, orchestrates and provides peace for their lives. He is watching over them as they sleep. He wakes them up in the morning. He nudges them to notice Him, just because He wants to be with them. Once my humans look to God, and they realize that He is with them, He comforts them.

When the distractions and difficulties of life surface, humans will need extra comfort, just as I do. When troubles happen, just as He had said they would in His book (the Bible), God calls out to my humans (and all His humans). They will hear Him if they are listening, and they either can envision themselves sitting at His feet, finding calm, or running full speed for His lap, where they know they will get the most comfort of all.

Getting more comfort from Daddy as he holds me and we pose!

God is pleased when my humans come to Him with a need or in prayer. He is also pleased as my humans continue to seek Him by digging their paws into His Word, just as my humans love it when I knead them with my paws. And, as my humans keep seeking Him, this dance of seeking and relating and being soothed through life continues. He continues to meet and exceed their needs as my humans respond to His signals—and all is well.

What About You?

Do you experience peace from God seeking and receiving His love? If not, you can. Ask Him to speak to you. Ask Him what He sees in you. Ask Him for wisdom or for whatever you need…

Just as you may be delighted to provide your human child or your fur child with his or her every need, God delights in providing for you. So go ahead, ask God for whatever you need, just like I ask my daddy for anything, anytime…

Meow for now,

Clive

Entertaining myself with my favorite toy—Mommy's hair tie!

8

SIMPLE ENTERTAINMENT

I am a pretty simple creature. Give me a lap, the companionship of my humans, some foodie, a head scratch, a cozy space to crawl into—and I'm a happy cat.

Even my entertainment is simple. I don't need any fancy cat toys—I have had them before. But do you know what my favorite toys are? My mommy's hair ties. She keeps them in her bathroom drawer. I know how to jump up there to get some.

Once a hair tie is on the floor, all I have to do is put my paw through it—and voila! Instant entertainment! It jumps around and moves down the hall. The hair tie dances with me. This toy is easier for me to keep up with than a bug or mice, which tend to be faster than me.

A hair tie plays with me at my pace. Once I am done playing with it—say if I need to take a cat nap or get a head scratch—a hair tie sits still. I love that it stays there, and that it is ready to play again when I am ready.

I also love to carry my round prey in my teeth. If my parents accidentally leave the toilet lid up, I drop my hair tie in the bowl and try to get it out again. But I'm not always very successful at retrieving it from the water. If I am successful, I usually make a wet mess, which irritates my humans.

Sometimes my humans have to help me get the hair tie out of the toilet. I don't like it when they have to help with this task, though, because then they throw that hair tie away. But my mommy has an endless supply of these toys in her drawer, and they are all the same, so I don't care if I lose one.

I know my humans love that I am entertained with such a simple thing. I also love that my humans love all kinds of simple entertainment like:

- Conversing casually

- Laughing together

- Dreaming about the future

- Singing their favorite songs to each other

- Relaxing, reading a book

- Staring at the stars from the patio

- Savoring a sunset, and

- Cuddling by a crackling fire

If you want to learn more about my humans' simple entertainment in nature, read their blog, *Hiking with Your Honey.*

What About You?

Is there any kind of simple entertainment that you enjoy? Do you like making work and other life tasks simpler? Are you doing something simple often enough to balance out the challenges of life? Could you come up with a plan that would enable you to spend more time on the simple things?

Be like me…enjoy something simple. If you can't think of anything, ask God to give you a new appreciation for something simple. Mommy says He helps her reframe her love for the simple things: like a walk around the block, smelling the flowers, rewatching a favorite movie, or cozying up with a good book about a fun character. I think this book about me fits that bill, don't you? I'm uber handsome, resourceful, smart, and loving—with just enough ornery-ness to make you laugh 🐱. I hope you are enjoying reading about me and my thoughts about humans, God, and foodie— which reminds me…it's time for my snack! I LOVE MY FOODIE!

Meow for now,

Clive

When I'm stressed, it's best to show off my tummy and beg for help!

9

Averting Distress for Something Better

Some days I find myself in distress! Can you relate? Here is what happens on those days:

I find myself crying incessantly. Nine out of 10 times, I cry this way when foodie is on my mind. I WANT MY FOODIE! As I cry, I pace if my humans are moving around doing something that doesn't involve feeding me or paying attention to me. Even when it's not my mealtime, I can easily become obsessed—and start meowing with great urgency—thinking about foodie.

I know that Mommy and Daddy go down the hallway when they get ready to leave. If they go that direction, I get so scared that they are leaving and will forget to feed me. I wonder if I will need to contact an animal rescue group if they don't feed me. I always look to see if Mommy has her laptop open so I can try to find a hunger hotline or something.

Someone else who sees clearly intervenes. What I don't know in my distressed moments is that too much of a good thing makes me sick. My humans have to ration my food—otherwise I eat too much of it. They are just concerned about me, and they don't want me to get heart disease or diabetes and die—because that would surely break their hearts.

The desperation gets replaced in my special place. I'm always amazed that Mommy and Daddy know me so well—and I'm so glad that they know what to do. They know that if I am distressed, all they have to do is to pick me up and put me on their laps.

33

Shifting my mindset to gratitude changes my outlook. Much of the time when I am crying, thinking I am going to starve, I am not really physically hungry. A 23-pound cat doesn't really "need" food. Knowing my humans love me usually calms me. It doesn't matter how upset I think I am. If for some reason Mommy and Daddy don't come to me right away, one tactic I try is plopping down on the floor, showing off my tummy, and positioning my paws in begging position. This pose often gets their attention. You can see why in my handsome photograph at the beginning of this musing!

When Mommy and Daddy pick me up and get me on their laps, the love I feel makes me purr and snort (I do both). I am no longer distressed. I eventually start kneading them with my paws and my motor roars. I now feel like a lion.

Mommy says watching my transformation from being distressed to at complete peace ministers to her frustrated, pent-up, things aren't happening fast enough, sometimes discouraged soul. She told me that she asked God to show her how she is sometimes like me begging for an extra meal before it is time to eat.

She sensed God answering her, saying,

> *Come to Me and let me support you as you rest in my arms, laying your head on My lap. Let Me show you that I've got this issue and ALL your cares.*
>
> *Stay snuggled up to Me, because just like you move when it is time to feed Clive, I will move you and gently scoop you up to walk you to where you need to be next. But, in the meantime, enjoy your place here—in my lap—letting Me lavish You with my love.*

Mommy responds: "Thank you Lord. I'm so grateful for Your words."

What About You?

Are you like me, wanting food, obsessing about how much you *think* you need something? Maybe ask God and other trusted friends to help you make sure your perspective is accurate.

Perhaps you can comfort yourself by going somewhere or doing something else that you know is good for you. As I've told you, Mommy says taking a walk and noticing something beautiful in creation soothes her soul. She just got back from a walk, and I can tell that she is more peaceful. She is already more thankful, and I can see the shift that has taken place in her attitude.

When your own attitude shifts, notice what happens to your body and your outlook.

Mommy says we can watch our spirits soar as we begin to enjoy where we are.

That Mommy of mine is pretty smart…and I know I'm just like her. 🐱

Meow for now,

Clive

Looking at Mommy when she was hanging out with me on the floor, just to love me where I'm at.

10

LOVING ME WHERE I'M AT

I've told you before about how I jump up on my humans' laps or climb up to their level by getting on top of something. I—like most cats—love to get up high whenever I can.

But sometimes, you know what? I just don't feel like jumping up anywhere. At those times I plop right down on the floor, whenever I feel like it.

Sometimes, I don't come when I'm called—although I usually respond to my name. At the very least, I give a short meow or sound, saying, "I heard you," in a friendly voice.

Sometimes, I long for my owners to come to me. In fact, I want Mommy and Daddy to make an effort to be with me. I love responding to my owners 90% of the time in dog-like fashion by coming to them—but I can't escape my feline DNA 100% of the time!

That feline design makes me sometimes aloof and want things my way. I've seen Mommy and Daddy not get along well every now and then too. When I asked Mommy about that, she says that sometimes humans like to have their own way as well—just like cats do.

Because Mommy understands me, and she is sympathetic to me being in "a mood," she does something wonderful. When I don't come to her when she calls me, and I just want to lie down on the floor, she comes to where I am to pet me!

It doesn't matter that she may have to lie down on the floor, squeezing her body between me and whatever piece of furniture is nearby. She still comes down to my level and lies there with me. Her coming to the floor makes me feel unconditionally loved and accepted. I'm so grateful.

I asked Mommy why she does this, and she says she is mirroring how God loves her. She wants me to feel the unconditional love that she feels from Him. God wanted to be with her (and all humans), so he sent His Son, Jesus, down from the level of being in Heaven to a lower level—as a human being on Earth. Mommy says that when she thinks of Jesus doing that just to be with her, she is in awe. She says she doesn't understand it…until she thinks of my Daddy, me, and her close friends—all of whom she would lie on the floor to hang out with.

With His action and this vision, God gave Mommy and me another glimpse of His love for us. He loves us how he wants us to love others. Here are some of His words:

> In your relationships with one another, have the same mindset as Christ Jesus: Who, being in very nature God, did not consider equality with God something to be used to his own advantage; rather, he made himself nothing by taking the very nature of a servant, being made in human likeness. And being found in appearance as a man, he humbled himself by becoming obedient to death—even death on a cross!
> (Philippians 2:5–8, NIV).

What About You?
Is there someone who may be "in a mood" that you could try to reach out to and go be with wherever he or she is? If you are like my mommy and daddy, you may remember a time when people got down on the floor to be with you when you needed it.

Mommy would always say to ensure you are protected and strong before you go to a difficult place to be with someone else. Ask God to strengthen you so that you can support another person.

In His Word, God says that there is a time and a season for everything. If you are struggling with depression and barely getting by, it may not be the time to lend a hand. If this isn't your season to support, but instead to heal and be supported, please don't feel bad or ashamed about where you are right now. God also tells us to use discernment and to be wise about timing. But if He is prompting you to help, because He wants you to help, He will equip you for that assignment.

And just like it was for my mommy to come down to be with me, it will be rewarding for you to meet another where he or she is at—even if it's on the floor.

Meow for now,

Clive

Expressing a not-so-pleasant
reaction to my humans!

11
TEMPERING UNPREDICTABLE REACTIONS

Even though I am loved well by my humans who seek me out wherever I am, at times, I have prickly reactions. I have these despite my best effort to be good. I have…

Good intentions. I want to love my humans well. I am always around them, and I don't make too much noise—well, unless I think I may be able to get some foodie—as I've said—and I'll say it again in case you forget—I LOVE MY FOODIE!

I also think I'm a wonderful pet because I don't require my humans to do much to take care of me. As I've shared, I'm pretty simple: feed me, clean my litter box, and I'm a happy cat—most of the time. But every once in a while, I have…

Unpredictable reactions. I get really snippy—with my teeth. My humans can be petting me, giving me the best head scratch that I was happy with less than one minute earlier. And then, out of the blue, pops a snip, which takes my humans by surprise. Sometimes a hand is pulled away, followed by a firm yet gentle slap on my head.

Another time I tend to get snippy is when I have just been fed. I wish my bowl was filled to the rim instead of rationed into the less than ½ cup portions I normally receive. I get scared when my parents walk near the door that they might leave and forget to feed me. It's not rational, because they DO feed me. I may even still have foodie in my bowl, but my reactions happen anyway sometimes. When this fear of them leaving overtakes me, I jump up and nip my humans' pants with my teeth.

When Mommy has pants on that are wide or flowy at the bottom, I especially like to jump up and grab them. When I do this, I get…

Loving discipline. Mommy gets mad when I jump on her, and she turns around, raises her voice a little, points her finger, and says "no" louder than her normal voice. Then she gives me a little pop on the head.

I know I have not been kind because she doesn't do that if I haven't hurt her. She doesn't discipline me if I meow instead of snip to let her know that I need comforting. There is no reason for me to fear telling my mommy I need help.

But for some reason, I still have fear, which can cause bad behavior. I wish I didn't get scared and react badly, but when Mommy and Daddy gently discipline me, I am reminded that hurting them out of fear is not okay. I am grateful that they help temper my moods and help me remember a better way to behave. They also foster…

Self-initiated corrective action. After they discipline me, when I know that I have done something wrong, I usually run away and hide in shame at first. Within a few minutes, I come out and want to be with my humans once again. I want to behave well and return to being the best pet ever.

I have also learned that if I can't be nice, I am likely overly tired and need sleep. I am pleased that, many times through a short catnap, I have found a way to temper my own mood—before parental discipline is necessary.

What About You?

Do you sometimes have reactions that you aren't proud of? Have you learned to mitigate them successfully or could you do better?

Mommy told me that God has some advice to help us have kinder reactions. He says in His book (the Bible):

> …Take every thought captive to obey Christ (2 Corinthians 10:5, ESV).

I don't know how to do that, but He will help you replace unkind or inappropriate thoughts with ideas and actions that are both beneficial to you and those around you.

Meow for now,

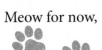

Clive

Bowing my head to pray
with my humans...

12
DOING MY PART, PART 1

I do my part to be useful, entertaining, and loving to my humans. I don't know why I do what I do—I'm just a cat, after all. But I thought I'd share with you what I do…do.

No, that isn't a typo—and yes—I do make doo-doo. So do you. Daddy would be proud of me with that dad joke—I'll have to tell him! I know he will laugh.

Now, *where was I?…*

Oh yes…what I do…do! Ha! I can't get enough of my own jokes!

Mommy is telling me to get to the point…Okay, okay! Here is what I do:

I serve as a bookstand. When my parents get up in the morning, they read the Bible and journal. I like to be right in the middle of the action, and their laps are only big enough for either the books or for me. So, what's our solution? The books lay on my back. As long as they scratch under my chin when they read, I am totally fine with these books resting on me. I love hearing their voices as they read, pray, and learn. I think I may be getting smarter by osmosis!

I bow my head and cross my paws in prayer as my humans pray. I want to be like them, so I imitate them. I am patient, and I listen. If I start to squirm too soon, they scratch my head once again—then I stay in their laps for a really long time!

Well, unless I happen to open my eyes and see a light reflection or a bug flying around. Then I have to go on the hunt! I have to get the bug so I can eat it. Getting rid of bugs is another job of mine that Mommy especially praises me for! She doesn't like bugs—but I think they are yummy. Plus, I get to demonstrate my hunting prowess when I eat one!

I come running when I am called. As I shared earlier, this behavior is unlike most other felines. When I hear one of my humans call my name, I can't help but run to them. I love to jump onto their laps so they can pet me. I love their companionship SO much—it's the best!

I'm starting to get tired thinking of all I do...so I better wrap this musing up. But let me first remember to ask about you. I hear my mommy's voice reminding me to include others in the conversation...so here it goes:

What About You?

Do you provide foundational support (like a bookstand) to others in your household, business, or community?

Have you asked God to lead you into something that is bigger than you, but that you could play a part in? Is He telling you to be still, to learn, or to assist another human? Or is He saying that it's time to get up and run for another purpose? If you are not sure which way to go, Mommy suggests quieting your mind as you wait for an answer.

In His Book, God says, "Call to Me, and I will answer you, and show you great and mighty things, which you do not know" (Jeremiah 33:3, NKJV).

Now that I've done my part to encourage you, it's way past my time for my cat nap!!

Meow for now,

Clive

Providing companionship to Mommy while she writes, touching her leg under one of my favorite furry blankets.

13

DOING MY PART, PART 2

Okay, I'm awake again. I've had maybe, uh, 10 catnaps in the last 24 hours. Maybe more. Who knows? I don't really count them because I take them whenever I want.

Now, however, it's time for me to continue my list of how I "do my part" in my family.

I provide constant companionship. I am here throughout the day for my work-at-home Mommy. When she decided to stay home after she moved to Tennessee and was working remotely, she was worried about feeling lonely. But there I was! And as she writes or edits, I've been with her every day since that day years ago. I'm touching her legs right now under one of my favorite furry blankets!

I entertain and converse. Since Mommy doesn't talk to many other humans during the business day like she used to, she entertains herself with all the dialog you are reading between us. Unless I'm hungry, I let her call me when she wants to see me so that I don't interrupt her too often.

I converse and interact with Daddy too. When he gets ready, he gets out his socks. We have a game in which I try to swat and bite his socks, and he tries to get them away from me. I "win" because I bite them before he grabs them to put them on. We play the same game with his belt, which he gets out next. It takes different tactics to "win" at the belt game because the belt is slick and heavy. But I still prevail and grab it with my paws! Daddy then pets me, proud of my success. After our games, he finishes getting dressed, and he talks to me as he continues to gather what he needs for the day.

Sometimes my mommy get confused when she hears Daddy talking to me. If Mommy says, "What did you say, Baby?" I know she thinks Daddy is talking to her. She does not call me baby. She has many nicknames for me, but Baby is reserved for Daddy. Daddy will then say, "I'm talking to Jack, Honey!" At any rate, I love that Daddy and I have our own conversations… I need male-to-male attention at times!

Both Mommy and me showing—and allowing—affection in a "mamma sandwich."

I show—and allow—affection. I've already told you about the extensive jumping up in my humans' laps, and how I constantly follow them around. But I haven't mentioned "mamma sandwiches." One way Mommy shows me her love is to lie her head on top of me. I purr with delight. She doesn't squash me—I am big, so I can take it. I'm including a picture so you can see.

I beg for foodie to help my humans. Both my mommy and daddy were in really good shape when they met, but they have found a few pounds in their marriage. They have to put on clothes since they don't have fur—well Daddy is somewhat furry—but I digress. My point is they don't want to have to buy bigger clothing, so they have to watch their food intake. I have convinced them that when I cry for food, I am really just helping them with their personal weight loss goals because if they give me some of their food, they will have less to eat themselves. (Am I a genius or what?) Helping them with their weight loss is the least I could do to give back to them for all they do for me! Underneath my clever veneer, though, they know that I actually just want more food. I LOVE MY FOODIE!

Wow. I'm getting tired reading all I do again…so I'd better ask…

What About You?

Mommy says God gives all humans and animals roles tailor-made for how He created each of us.

Do you know your purpose and what you are created to do? If not, no problem—just ask God.

If you know what your current "part" or job is, are you doing it with excellence and joy, like God would want you to do?

When you do what God calls you to do in the manner in which He calls you to do it, His love shines through you.

Don't take my word for it; I'm just a cat. So, I've copied some of God's words from the Bible so that you can read them for yourself.

> For we are His workmanship, created in Christ Jesus for good works (Ephesians 2:10, NKJV).

> Whatever you do in word or deed, do all in the name of the Lord Jesus (Colossians 3:17, NKJV).

> So all of us who have had that veil removed can see and reflect the glory of the Lord. And the Lord—who is the Spirit—makes us more and more like him as we are changed into his glorious image (2 Corinthians 3:18, NLT).

That's more than enough for today! It's FINALLY time for another cat nap.

Good night, and meow for now!

Clive

Looking cute, encouraging my humans to get in bed with me and rest!

14

DOING MY PART, PART 3

After a bit more rest, I thought of even more ways I "do my part" as a member of my family…

I comfort my parents when they don't feel good. Today Mommy had to lie down because she was sick. I can always tell, somehow. I know I just need to lay there with her, and I gently lick her hands. I then nestle my head into her hand and go to sleep with her. I know that my presence and companionship helps her rest comfortably.

I serve as a second alarm clock. Sometimes my humans are still tired when they know it is time to get up early in the morning during the week, and they struggle getting up. My internal clock is really good, and I do my part to help get them up—when it's time.

Some of the time, though, I don't wait until morning to get something I want from my humans. If I want more foodie or water in the middle of the night, I go to Mommy. She doesn't get mad at me if I wake her up. If I wake Daddy up in the middle of the night, on the other hand, and it's not an emergency, I will likely experience what he calls, "the left foot of fellowship." I'm a 23-pound burly hunk of feline, though, and Daddy doesn't kick hard in his sleep, so if I happen to forget and I bother him, I will be okay!

When it is actually the appropriate time for my humans to get up, I go to Daddy, because Daddy can help me get Mommy up if she is resistant.

Me meowing multiple times is how I wake up my humans, letting them know that it is time for our morning couch time. As I've said, that's when we read Scripture and pray over our day and listen to what Big Daddy (God) may be saying to us. If my humans don't respond right away, I climb on top of them and meow in their ears. That action will always get them up, and finally, our day can get started.

Sometimes, though, on the weekends, if Daddy is still tired, he sometimes falls back asleep. If Daddy wants to go back to sleep, Mommy happily joins him. I then decide it must be a good idea to take a few more cat naps. I will then try again to wake them up later.

I make happy noises when I sleep, encouraging my parents to rest when they need it. Many cats are nocturnal, but I am not. Once it is dark, after I have enjoyed my evening meal, I want to go to sleep. My humans, on the other hand, may have work or writing to do. They sit up in their bed, and I lie at their feet. I make happy noises as I dream about them petting me, enjoying another meal, or embarking on courageous cat adventures. I think that when they see me relaxed and comfortable, it makes them want to sleep. They are reminded to push through what they have to get done but also to remember that only so much can be done in a day. Soon they will finish their work—and call it a night.

I have done my part once again.

On either Saturday or Sunday, Mommy and Daddy take a break all day long, just as Big Daddy did.

> By the seventh day God had finished the work he had been doing; so
> on the seventh day he rested from all his work (Genesis 2:2, NIV).

They take lots of cat naps on that day, and I join them willingly—once again doing my part.

What About You?

If you are like my humans, some days—especially on the weekends—your "part" may be to rest and recover. Even if you are up against a deadline, you may be best served by recharging your batteries.

What recharges you? What do you find restful? Do you have enough "scheduled" rest time? The alarm clock will go off on Monday morning or other times when the "must do now" time inevitably comes. That's why Mommy and I want to encourage you to take down time as often as you need it.

Meow for now,

Clive

A close up of my peaceful face during one of my many cat naps.

15

THE POWER OF A CAT NAP

Remember how I said that I help my parents go to sleep at night and that I rest with them willingly on weekends? I do that, but as I've probably already mentioned, that's not the only time I rest…

I take cat naps all day long—I need a break from exploring, being a human companion, playing with hair ties, begging for creamy beverages, and even purring. Too much of a good thing can be tiring.

Whenever my eyes get droopy, I let myself sleep. I get even better sleep when I cuddle up to one of my humans. I love it when they relax with me. It makes me feel like I am still doing my part for them—and taking care of myself too.

I know my fellow felines and I wish our human friends would learn this trick of sleeping whenever they feel tired. How much better moods would they be in if they all rested for just 30 minutes whenever they had the opportunity? How many more head scratches would we get if humans took a nap and had more energy? How much better would humans feel if they weren't overly tired, stressed, or emotional?

My Case Study—My Mommy
Mommy took a cat nap today. She didn't sleep well last night because of some ongoing issues in her shoulder, and because she was thinking about some stressful work situations.

Before she rested, she was dragging, fighting to stay awake, and unable to complete her task or be fully focused. I knew she was not at peace. I did my part and started to snooze. After she saw me relaxed, she got up from the couch and moved to the bed to lie down. As soon as I heard her moving, I got up and followed her. I jumped up on the bed, snuggled up near her, and then she dozed off peacefully to the sound of my purrs.

After her cat nap, she:

1. Rocked through her task list once again.
2. Was no longer warring with her eyelids that previously felt like bricks.
3. Came up with new writing ideas, overcoming the writer's block she had earlier in the day.
4. Saw the best way to organize the rest of her day.
5. Received clarity about how to deal with some difficult challenges.

Best of all, she was happier and back to her smiley, easy-going self, ready to pet me once again—AND make dinner. That means human plates will be available for me to lick in the not-too-distant future! So, I'm happier too!

What About You?

Have you benefited from taking a cat nap if your eyes are heavy or if you are overwhelmed? If so, how did you feel before and after you rested?

Mommy says that it helps to ask God to clear her mind so that she can rest well—even for a short cat nap. She is doing what He says in His book, which says,

> Cast all your anxiety on him, because he cares for you
> (1 Peter 5:7, ESV).

Jesus echoes His daddy's sentiments:

> "Come to Me, all who are weary and burdened, and I will give you rest" (Matthew 11:28, NASB).

All this talk about naps is making me tired again! Time to practice what I preach!

Good night again—and meow for now!

Clive

Enjoying being cradled in my daddy's hand.

16
RESTING IN HIS HANDS

In my last musing, I mused on the power of cat naps. Now I am going to share where and how I rest if I am upset and need to regain peace.

I cradle my head in my daddy's hand.

I snuggle up to his hand, and I let him rub me to comfort my anxious soul.

I don't have to wonder how or if I am going to get fed—

I just know to cradle my head in his hand.

I don't have to worry about being alone—

I just know to cradle my head in his hand.

I don't have to seek something elusive I can't find—

I just need to cradle my head in his hand.

I don't have to worry about scratching my own itches—

I just need to cradle my head in his hand.

Just like Daddy enables me to rest in his hand, Big Daddy (God) enables you to give your cares and worries to Him. No matter if your concerns are relational, vocational, physical, or emotional, He's got you covered. So, I'll give this advice to any human willing to listen: *Cradle your head in Big Daddy's hand.* He will soothe you, love you, and enable you to rest. He will speak to you, giving you words of comfort, guidance, and direction! Just think about how BIG His hand is if He can hold a whole human in it!

His hand is actually even bigger than that, though. As the old Sunday school song tells us, "He's got the whole world in His hands."

So, if He's holding everything together, take heart! He's got your life in His hands too.

What About You?

Have you tried cradling your head in your Heavenly Father's hand? If not, I encourage you to allow the truth of these words from the Bible to soothe your soul as you consider resting your head in His hand…

> Cast your cares on him, and He will sustain you (Psalm 55:22, NIV).

> So do not worry, saying, "What shall we eat?' or 'What shall we drink?' or 'What shall we wear?'" (Matthew 6:31, NIV).

> Don't be afraid, for I am with you. Don't be discouraged, for I am your God. I will strengthen you and help you. I will hold you up with my victorious right hand (Isaiah 41:10, NLT).

It's once again time for me to rest in Daddy's (and Big Daddy's) hand!

Meow for now,

Clive

One of my favorite interruptions...
the "mamma sandwich."

17
INVALUABLE INTERRUPTIONS

Hello again, humans. I'm feeling a little on the philosophical side lately. So, in this musing, I'll share a reflection about a famous quote from my namesake, C.S. Lewis.

He said: "The truth is of course that what one regards as interruptions are precisely one's life."—Collected Works of C. S. Lewis (1994)[4]

I know that my entire life is made up of interruptions. I was created to have my prowling and napping interrupted by the companionship of my humans—and I am thrilled by it each time because I love to be with them.

When I think about them interrupting my cat naps or any feline activities, I could be frustrated. After all, I never know what my people are going to do, nor am I ever in control of their actions. My experience is different, though. As I've said, I'm happy with my humans and most of their interruptions! In one of my many cat naps, I could be dreaming of playing with a mouse, and a human interruption happens. Sometimes Mommy interrupts my nap because I look so cuddly. She may pet me, or she may use me as a pillow. As I've told you before, that's what she calls a "mamma sandwich," and when she gives me one, I purr loudly—for a while. I love the "mamma sandwich"—but I don't love it forever. I don't like to admit that her head will eventually squash my burley-hunk-of-feline love, but it will. So, after several loving minutes, I interrupt the "mamma sandwich" with a polite meow, and she moves.

When Mommy wakes me up from a cat nap, despite me being initially groggy, I am so excited to follow her wherever she is going.

I do more than follow, though. I interrupt her back by trying to stand in front of her so that she will stop and pet me along her way.

If she goes to the kitchen, I interrupt her from cooking or doing dishes with begging and meowing because I am sure that she will make something yummy and share a little portion of it with me.

Speaking of food, I even interrupt myself during my morning meal. After a couple bites, I stop eating to greet my humans affectionately for a few minutes. Once I have loved on them, I go back and devour the rest of my foodie. I LOVE MY FOODIE!

As you may have gathered by now, I am not stressed by interruptions…I like them! Sometimes I wonder why humans are so distressed when their loving Heavenly Father causes interruptions. He is bigger than they are, just like my humans are bigger than me. He says in His book that He causes all things to work together for good (Romans 8:28). With those words, God sounds just like my humans, who are always looking out for what's good for me.

Maybe humans who are stressed by interruptions would do well to make a slight shift in perspective. Maybe the frustrations can become joys…and maybe they will begin to treasure the interruptions—like I do.

What About You?
Do you see the silver lining in unexpected interruptions? Sometimes appreciating interruptions is as simple as anticipating the blessings from a new situation. If you struggle with interruptions, ask God to show you a purpose in deviating your plans. Just like He does with me, He's ready to bless you from interruptions too!

Meow for now,

Clive

I just jumped onto Mommy's lap in the midst of her Bible reading—I know she can't lift me right now with a frozen shoulder. She always wants me with her, though, and I'm happy to oblige!

18

ANATOMICAL INTERRUPTIONS

I had a few more thoughts about my namesake's quote on interruptions that I also shared in my last musing. Just so you don't have to turn back a few pages, I've printed it again for you…

"The truth is, of course, that what one regards as interruptions are precisely one's life."
—Collected Works of C. S. Lewis (1994)

Some of you refined humans may turn your nose up at what I'm about to share, but I don't! I like to talk about EVERYTHING!

Bathroom breaks. I am often interrupted from cat naps when my mommy gets up because of regular anatomical interruptions. Yes, I am talking about when she has to go to the bathroom. I always follow close behind her into "the loo." I love the feel of the cozy rug by the commode and lying on top of her feet. I purr with delight when I sit there.

When I talked to Mommy about these anatomical interruptions, she said that she often welcomes the bathroom break, not just to relieve herself but also to shift her thoughts. She says that she may be perplexed by a problem, and the simple act of moving to another room can be enough of a change to help a new idea come. Therefore, she says that sometimes the change of scenery caused by this daily anatomical interaction contributes to keeping more than just physical things moving! (Oh that Mommy of mine; she can be funny!)

Bathroom "surprises." My parents also find an "interruption" from me if they leave me by myself for more than a day or two. Soon after they return home, they find my "interruption" on their walk through the house. Yes, I leave them a special poop present—it's how I best show that I don't like it when they leave. It seems to work—because they usually stay home for a while after I give them one.

Once they are home, they talk about the adventures they had while they were gone. One time, Daddy talked about their search for a bathroom near Tennessee's Rock Is-

Mommy and Daddy are chasing water-falls...but an "interruption" awaits!

land State Park, where they had seen one of the state's largest waterfalls.

They ended up finding a fabulous restaurant right on the river in the middle of nowhere as they were walking. The owner let them in to use the bathroom even through the restaurant was closed. It turns out a chef from New York City opened this restaurant in the middle of nowhere. There is a line there at 5 p.m. most evenings. Because the restaurant is small, if you don't get there at 5 p.m., you may not get a table for a few hours.

As they approached the restaurant that first time, Mommy and Daddy saw another anatomical interruption that interrupted their own quest to relieve themselves. They saw a cow in a pasture nursing her calf. Because Mommy grew up in suburbia and lived in downtown Chicago before she moved to Tennessee, she had never seen a nursing cow before. Daddy grew up in a rural area, so he had seen cows nurse. However, it was still a fun anatomical interruption for both of them on their way to take care of their own anatomical interruption!! Ha!

Mommy and Daddy came back and enjoyed the restaurant that evening, and they have returned a few times since—even though the restaurant is two hours away from where we live. Sometimes life is just not convenient. Mommy and I learned about that recently when she was…

Compensating for Physical Limitations. One of the more difficult anatomical interruptions for both Mommy and me is that as I write this musing, she has a frozen shoulder. She can't lift her arm up above being parallel to the floor, nor can she hold much weight with that arm. This physical issue "interrupts" one of our favorite rituals. She used to pick me up every day to hold me, and we would dance to one of her favorite songs. I would purr the whole time! As long as the song is on the slower side, I don't get too jostled!

Before her frozen shoulder, she would also scoop me up when I was in a deep sleep to carry me if she wanted to move to another room. Even though I am a burley-hunk-of-feline love, as you can probably tell, I never outgrow receiving love from my human. If I am just in a light cat nap, I normally hear her and move with her.

But if I happen to not wake up, she gently pets me and says, "Come on Clive," followed by a cute noise she makes with her mouth. I get up—I love hearing that noise. I jump up onto her wherever she goes, and once she gets settled again, whether she is sitting or lying down, I get on top of her.

Daddy also does his part too to help overcome the anatomical interruption of Mommy's shoulder. He picks me up and supports all my weight. Mommy can then simply lean in to hug us. Brilliant! With Daddy doing the heavy lifting, Mommy's desire to hold me standing up is fulfilled. We dance or stand there for a few minutes. Daddy often sings to Mommy, and I just purr. This special time is what we call a "parent sandwich!" We love it, but we may not have thought of it without mommy's injury.

What About You?

What interruptions have you experienced that have turned into blessings? As we have discussed, all interruptions—for whatever reason—can be frustrating at first. However, we encourage you to take heart! God redeems as He accomplishes His purposes in the interruptions. He has plans we may not be aware of, and He encourages us to be patient. Take a look at these two verses from God's book:

> A man's heart plans his way, But the LORD directs his steps
> (Proverbs 16:9, NKJV).

> Wait for the LORD; be strong and take heart and wait for the LORD
> (Psalm 27:14, NIV).

Time for me to interrupt this musing to go beg for more foodie!

Meow for now,

Clive

Me...molding a box to be just my size!

19

SOMETIMES YOU NEED TO CHANGE OR MOVE YOUR BOX

Conventional Placement Doesn't Always Work

When we lived in a small apartment, my humans finally gave in and moved my litter box (at least during the daytime) to a more central location. I didn't like my box placement in the laundry room behind the door. I had to go too far away from my humans to get in there. I like to be able to see and hear everything that is going on. I also don't like closed doors, and I didn't like my box near those big machines.

I expressed my need for my box to be moved in the clearest way I know how: by leaving my poop present in the hallway on the carpet.

Once they gave in and moved my box each morning, we were both happy. I could see them, and I always went in my box.

One Size Does Not Fit All

Another breakthrough with my box happened after I had a neighbor come in and check on me when Mommy and Daddy were out of town. She noticed something that my humans hadn't noticed, just because they see me every day. Everything about me is familiar to them.

The neighbor noticed that I was struggling inside my box because it had a lid. I am about twice as big as most cats. The litter boxes with lids are made for average-sized cats, who are generally under 15 pounds. But as I have said often, I am a special 23-pound-hunk-of-feline love! I am physically bigger—and I have an extra special loving heart.

When the neighbor shared my struggle with my humans, they took the lid off my box. It was so liberating! Doing my business is easier because I can move my body around however I need to—even with my unique differences.

Human Boxes

Sometimes humans need to move their various "boxes" too—or they may need to ask for help to have their boxes moved. Mommy is only my mommy as I write because she chose to move two of her "boxes" just before we met. She moved her living "box" from the concrete jungle of downtown Chicago to the greenery and serenity of the outskirts of Nashville, Tennessee. She wanted to move from colder Chicago to a climate where she could hike and walk outside for most of the year without extreme discomfort.

She moved her work "box" from a stressful, director-level, full-time position to having a freelance writing and editing business where she could have more control over her schedule and take more breaks—with me! Her improved lifestyle made it easier for her to sit with God for every morning for an hour or longer, either on the deck or in her favorite rocking chair. God helped her recover from her formerly frenzied lifestyle, and He helped her prepare for a healthier, slower paced life.

She was able to get healthy, and her energy returned—and I supported her the entire way. A year later, after she moved her "boxes," she met my daddy. Since Mommy and Daddy have been married, they have moved three times, enabling us to spread out. Although I don't enjoy a new living "box" immediately after we move, soon I come to love it. As I've said before, I just want to be where my humans are. If they are happier in their new "box," so am I.

What About You?

Have you ever felt the need to change things up to get a fresh perspective? Have you ever thought you were trapped or caged by boxes that aren't your shape? Maybe it is time to step out and try a different "box" or two. Is it time for new work, a new place to live, or some new friendships? And, although it generally isn't wise to turn your life upside down in a day, it may be time to try taking baby steps in a new direction to help you plan out a new course.

If you want to move one of your boxes, consider asking God for help. He promises to lead His humans to good "boxes!" Here are just a couple examples from His Book.

The land you have given me is a pleasant land. What a wonderful inheritance! (Psalm 16:6, NLT).

Then my people will live in a peaceful settlement, In secure dwellings, and in undisturbed resting places (Isaiah 32:18, NASB).

I'm thankful for my resting place, so I'm going to take advantage of it by enjoying another catnap.

Meow for now,

Clive

20
TAKE MORE BREAKS, MOMMY!

My Mommy works as a writer and editor, and as I've told you before, she is blessed to get to stay home with me.

Although I love having her here, I don't like it when she feels rushed because of a deadline. Not only does she seem to feel pressure at those times, but also, she doesn't have as much time to play with me or to write my thoughts as she does on other days.

She and I both function better when she has more margin. She is nicer to me and not as frenzied.

When I see her in duress, I try to help her. I sit on top of her book print outs and any other papers as much as possible. Now that she has an injury, I also know that it can be hard for her to get me off of the papers that she needs. As you know by now, I am a burly 23-pound-hunk-of-feline love. I know I have said that many times—but this important fact bears repeating!

The bottom line is that I can help make her breaks longer! Genius, right? I think so!

I also want to say, that I'm a single cat genius, and I'm taking inquiries for my soulmate! Well, maybe. I actually don't know if I want to share my castle… No—I don't. Scratch that idea.

Where was I? Oh yes, I remember. I was telling you how I purposely sit on top of Mommy's work to make her take a break and pet me. I have to be THE CENTER OF EVERYTHING!

What happens if she doesn't heed my advice and take a break? What do I do if she pushes me off her papers, and she keeps working?

Well, I get kind of obnoxious. One time, I marched right between the camera and my mommy on an online conference call. Fortunately, that client loves cats and had been asking to see what I looked like. My reputation had proceeded me, and I took over the entire meeting, because everyone at the virtual table "oohed" and "awwed" at my cuteness.

I thought the meeting went very well, but Mommy doesn't do work for that client anymore, so maybe the meeting didn't go as well as I thought. I guess I should be more careful. But she would be wise take more breaks—and when she takes them, she would be wiser to take a cat nap with me!

I have even tried to tell her that napping is spiritual. After all, Big Daddy's book says:

> It is vain for you to rise up early, to take rest late, to eat the bread of [anxious] toil—for He gives [blessings] to His beloved in sleep (Psalm 127:3, AMPC).

I'm not a theologian, but I listen to Big Daddy! Hint, Mommy! She's not yet listening, so I'll ask…

What About You?
Do you have enough margin in your day?

How do you take enough mental breaks to cope with life's unexpected deadlines and curveballs? Does someone have to force you to stop in that scenario? If so, could you consider a strategy to satisfy your need for periodic mental pauses?

If family members (including pets) are distracting, are there ways you can influence them to make a change that might benefit everyone? Could you get children or pets to play with a mind-engaging toy, for example? Hair tie, anyone? 🐱

Meow for now,

Clive

This is my favorite bag—my carrier! When my humans
get it out, I get to go with them!

21

I'm in the Bag

I can get a little freaked out when my humans pack. It's likely because I know that something is changing. I really don't understand why they don't take me with them.

One time when a suitcase was open with their things in it, I had a brilliant idea: Anytime Mommy or Daddy moved toward the door, where the suitcase was, I jumped into it! That way, they know I want to come, and they would be more inclined to take me with them! With me in the bag, they would not be able to close their suitcase, and then they wouldn't have their belongings, and they would have to stay here. Either way, I win!

When my humans have left in the past—even if it is just for a few days—they have taken *sooo* much of our house with them!

They usually travel with 10 bags—no that's not a typo with an extra 0 at the end— that's TEN bags. Mommy says it keeps them more organized because everything has its own compartment.

I know…I have tried to tell them…the number of bags is excessive, and they don't need to go in the first place. My humans sometimes even get a cart to carry all their stuff!

Daddy used to be more reasonable, carrying just a few bags, but because the pain in his wrists and arms started acting up, he goes along with each bag being smaller and lighter.

Well—except for his suitcase. He keeps that pretty full. I'm lying in his suitcase now. He says if he has to carry it, it might as well be nearly full.

What in the world is in all these bags, you may ask? My humans pack:

- A book bag

- A vitamin bag

- A food bag

- A hot beverage bag

- Two bathroom bags

- Two suitcases

- A technology bag

- An emergency bag (with first aid, a way to make a fire, spare toilet paper, and a water filter)

You may be able to see why packing and unpacking is time consuming for my humans! They said they are done with adventures for the time being. I know that I am glad that they plan to be here for a while. But as long as this suitcase is out, and there is a possibility that they might leave, I'm staying in it—just in case.

In my daddy's suitcase...

I have tried to tell Mommy and Daddy to become more minimalist...after all, none of us can take anything with us to Heaven. And although Mommy and Daddy are concerned with eternal things, I think they still have some work to do to apply the following message from Big Daddy's Book. In fact, the following are Big Brother Jesus' words:

Do not lay up for yourselves treasures on earth, where moth and rust destroy and where thieves break in and steal, but lay up for yourselves treasures in heaven, where neither moth nor rust destroys and where thieves do not break in and steal. For where your treasure is, there your heart will be also (Matthew 6:19–21, ESV).

What About You?

- Do you take too much stuff with you when you travel—or not enough?

- Can you easily find what you want when you are away?

- Is there one of my humans' bags that you may decide to add to your travel list?

- Is there something you know you want to take on your next trip, but you don't have yet? Perhaps it's time to order it now!

Since I really don't like to leave my house that often, I think I'll take another cat nap and dream of a grand cat and mouse adventure.

Meow for now,

Clive

Me going after my passion—a taste of one of my human's protein shakes.

22
GOING AFTER YOUR PASSIONS

What is one of my favorite things other than loving my humans? It's my humans' protein shakes. I love them. I go crazy for them. I hear the blender, and I run from anywhere in the house to come make sure that I get some of this thick, yummy liquid treat.

As my humans make their protein shakes, I get right behind them and beg by getting up on my hind legs. I paw my Mommy or Daddy's legs repeatedly as one of them blends this delightful concoction. They make me get down and wait, but then I start meowing at the top of my lungs.

Why do I keep meowing? Because I don't give up—I am not a quitter! I howl and cry and carry on until they give me a little taste in a small bowl.

And, why do they give this shake to me? Because it is delicious and nutritious. They wish they hadn't let me taste a shake in the first place. Since I am overweight and they both lost weight drinking these shakes, however, they didn't think the shakes would hurt me.

I don't think I've lost any weight because they only give me a few licks. My parents, on the other hand, drink more than eight ounces of this concoction twice a day. But I don't care that my amount of this liquid is limited. I am passionate about this shake because it tastes so good! I admit, I am kind of driven by my appetite. After all, I am just a cat, but there is a lesson for humans in my behavior—and, you guessed it, I'm going to share it!

The lesson is to be persistent and to go after your passion! I remember once when Mommy had a large project that she had wanted to do for quite some time, and although she was having technical difficulties, she persisted, asking Big Daddy (God) to help her. She finally found someone to partner with to make it possible to get the project done. She was motivated, and she kept trying. She also knew when to ask for help, recognizing that her passion would not be accomplished without another person.

So let me encourage you today, don't give up as you face challenges if you are going after something good. Challenges generally get the most difficult just as you are on the cusp of breaking through the barriers. Your goal may be attainable with just one more try. Or, just like He did for Mommy, Big Daddy may bring someone along who has just the skills you need to take you across the finish line.

What About You?
What are you passionate about? Are you driven by behaviors that are good for you—or will benefit you in the end? Are you persistent when something that you want is so close that you can taste it? Have you been blessed by another person who either had the skills to help you or who showed you how to finish?

If you are tired or discouraged in the midst of a big project, ask Big Daddy to help you keep going.

> So let's not allow ourselves to get fatigued doing good. At the right time we will harvest a good crop if we don't give up, or quit. Right now, therefore, every time we get the chance, let us work for the benefit of all, starting with the people closest to us in the community of faith (Gal. 6:9–10, MSG).

Meow for now,

Clive

Sitting patiently, waiting for Mommy and Daddy to be done writing so they will give me their full attention!

23
LESSONS IN FAIRNESS AND PATIENCE

I love both of my humans so much. When they are home and writing, I try to sit where I can see them. I lie on the floor in between them. Or I go to each of them for attention, especially when I think it's time to eat…I LOVE MY FOODIE!

But do you know what my favorite time with them is? It's when they snuggle together. Tonight, when Daddy came home, he laid down next to Mommy in the bed for about 20 minutes before they went to a Bible study. I got up right in between them, and I purred my loudest, roaring purr. I snorted, hummed, and sighed with wondrous delight. Then they had to get up and go, though. I was a little sad.

Now they are both back home, writing. Mommy is typing my thoughts, and Daddy is sharing his story about when he knew he wanted my Mommy to be his Honey. I wish these words would flow faster because I want their full attention—and I want them to give me more foodie!

So here I am, doing my best to "roll over and play cute" on the floor. I let out a playful sigh to get one of them to notice me. Since they keep looking at those silver half boxes with black keys, I go to Daddy's legs and howl a few times. I roll over on top of his feet. He is focused and not looking…bummer. Let me try Mommy…

After neither one of them notice me, I put on a scowl of disappointment, and my meow turns more to a low growl. I realize that more foodie is not going to be available for me to chomp in the near future.

But I can't give up! I try again. I jump up into Mommy's lap. I give her a few kneads on her blanket, a few licks on her arms, and then I give her a slight nibble—just so she knows I am waiting. She still doesn't respond, but I know I can't hurt her, or I will get in trouble. So, I start kneading again. That loving action enables me to distract myself from my foodie quest—and I am able to do what I do best—loving my humans! I still have to wait patiently for them, though!

Mommy doesn't make me wait too long. She says she has empathy for me because sometimes she gets impatient with her Heavenly Father the way that I get impatient with her. Like me, she also really wants what she wants—and she wants it now. But then she remembers that He knows what is best for her. After a sufficient, cat-like tantrum, she relaxes, waiting for God, remembering His instructions to His children that she read in His book.

> Therefore, as God's chosen people, holy and dearly loved, clothe yourselves with compassion, kindness, humility, gentleness and patience. Bear with each other and forgive one another if any of you has a grievance against someone. Forgive as the Lord forgave you. And over all these virtues put on love, which binds them all together in perfect unity (Colossians 3:12–14, NIV).

These words remind Mommy to have patience, and she, like all humans, has to ask if she's being fair. Sometimes, she gets easily offended, which isn't fair to others. She has to forgive because the Lord forgave her. Remembering both how Jesus forgave her—and how He didn't do anything before His Father told Him to at the right time—helps her remain patient and fair.

What About You?
Are there ways you can be like me and show fairness to two people at one time? Or, do you find being patient difficult? Perhaps consider that God will only share what we need for each day, as Jesus says…

> Give your entire attention to what God is doing right now, and don't get worked up about what may or may not happen tomorrow. God will help you deal with whatever hard things come up when the time comes (Matthew 6:34, MSG).

Taking this advice, I am going to practice NOT getting worked up to help me be fair and patient moving forward. I am going to go relax on my favorite blanket, and either doze off or take a bath…one of these strategies keeps me calm every time.

Meow for now,

Clive

Raising a paw in delight, celebrating
two special occasions.

24

CELEBRATING THE JOURNEY

Today I am having a great time and lifting my paw because my Mommy, Daddy, and I are celebrating two special occasions. It's National Cat Day, and we are celebrating our favorite baseball team winning the first two World Series games!

Representing My Kind Well

Happy cats unite!

Daddy says that, in general, it seems that men aren't fans of felines. I'm out to change that travesty, especially on National Cat Day. He also says that if more men knew me, they might give more cats a chance.

That's because I am just pleasant to be around, Daddy says. As you know by now, I am a loving, loyal companion. I am funny. I get myself in all kinds of positions. I show off as I pose for the camera. I make all kinds of noises—a purr, an extra satisfied purr-snort (yes, I add the snort to the end of a purr when I'm extra happy), a grunt, a light sigh, a soft whimper, and a harrowing howl. Probably my most common noise is an agreeable meow…which is how I join the conversation when my parents are conversing or hanging out with me.

Special Occasions Change Our Routine

I'm enjoying this game on TV that has us up to midnight. We are an early-to-bed, early-to-rise family on most nights, and we rarely watch TV.

I am finding it fun to hear the sound of a bat hitting a ball, to chase that ball with my eyes, and to watch the guys on the screen run. Every so often, my parents even jump up and down. It's fun to see them so excited!

Let me explain my mommy's enthusiasm… She grew up going to baseball and football games in her hometown with her dad and siblings. In fact, she wanted to be a sports TV anchorwoman when she was eight years old. Although she no longer wants that much of her life to be consumed by sports, she still considers herself a sports fan.

She doesn't watch baseball throughout the season because there are so many games. She does watch about half of her favorite football team's games, and she tunes into the sweet 16 of college basketball if her alma mater is still playing. When she can't watch the games throughout the season, she still checks the scores and the standings.

Mommy says that one day, after a big game, she heard a sermon in which the pastor gently pointed out that the congregation doesn't seem to get as excited about cheering for God as they do rooting for their favorite sports team.

Even though, as I've mentioned, Mommy sits with God each morning, she was challenged by the pastor's words. Are she and Daddy as excited, jumping up and down about what God has done for them like they are when their favorite team does something great? Mommy admits that they do not show as much enthusiasm for God as she does about one of her teams winning.

After that sermon, Mommy said she wants to learn to, more consistently and exuberantly, celebrate God with as much enthusiasm as she celebrates her teams. This kind of celebration is likely what He desires because He says:

> O magnify the LORD together, And let us lift up His name together (Psalm 34:3, AMP).

Mommy says she thinks magnifying the Lord might be like jumping up and down and high fiving your friends or family when God does something amazing in your life. I'm just a cat, but that sounds right to me!

> I will praise the name of God with song
> And magnify Him with thanksgiving (Psalm 69:20, AMP).

Mommy and Daddy do like to sing to the Lord together, both at church, and together at times in our home. I love to hear them sing together! I also know Mommy starts her day writing what she is grateful to God for in her journal. She mentioned, though, that magnifying the Lord means doing this out loud for others to hear. That's what she says she will work on moving forward.

What About You?

What special moments and pastimes are you celebrating today? Why not celebrate your own furry friends or cheer on your favorite team? Could you find more joy appreciating the creatures or people God has made—or by commemorating victorious moments? Just like He wants Mommy to do, God would love for you to celebrate Him and what He's done in your life!

Meow for now,

Clive

I teach my humans life lessons every day—even in the midst of a move.

25
COUNTRY LIVING WITH CRITTERS

I remember when my parents moved from a city apartment to a small country house. After I got over the traumatic experience of my entire world being torn apart, I grew to really love that country house.

It felt like a homecoming of sorts, because when I first met my mommy, she lived with two other ladies in a country home. I had missed the panoramic views and watching the birds—and when I got to enjoy these sights again, I was happy.

My favorite part of that new home was that my parents let me sleep on the bed with them for the first time—all night long! I also loved how cool the uncarpeted floors were on my furry belly! Mommy had area rugs and blankets, though, which I loved if I felt like getting cozy and warm.

BUT THEN…COMPETING CRITTERS!
First, a raccoon lived under our house. I know those things can hurt me, but luckily my Daddy is kind of Daniel Boone like—so he trapped the raccoon and took him away.

Next, a possum took the raccoon's place. If my humans knew then what they knew now, they would have kept that possum, because those ugly beasts eat ticks.

Later, squirrels scurried above our heads between the ceiling and the roof. We were trying to take a nap one Sunday, and these noisy nut-seekers were so loud that they were disturbing our peace. Well, Daddy wasn't going to stand for that, and he went outside to catch those critters in a hurry! I'm not sure what Daddy did, but we haven't heard them since!

Then ants and worms invaded my "party in the potty." I love to go to the loo whenever one of my humans do, so that's what Mommy calls our time together there. I know Mommy wishes that I would eat the bugs and worms, but I think worms are gross—just like she does. Speaking of the potty, we had to get a new one. Yep, for at least three days, my humans had no indoor plumbing. It was pretty gross, and they were gone a lot. At least they didn't try to use my box! They are too big!

And last but not least—the worst critters of all—FLEAS and TICKS!. These monsters must have been mad when Daddy got rid of all the other critters, and they found their way to me. I itched everywhere, and I got medicine. Unfortunately, that medicine made me really sick, and Mommy and Daddy had to take me to the Kitty ER. That was scary, but then that vet gave me a different kind of medicine. It took a few

Daddy trapped this possum under our country house shortly after we moved in.

days to work, and Mommy and Daddy had to wash everything in sight. So, for a few more days, my cozy home was kind of crazy.

But I was okay dealing with all these critters because Mommy and Daddy were with me and loving on me.

What About You?

Have you ever had any unwelcome four-legged critters, mice, or bugs invade your space? Take a minute or two to recall what you did to reclaim your home…and if you have a great tip or idea, pass it on to others!

If you are currently struggling with unwanted pests, I say, don't let the distractions get you down. You—and your loved ones—can defeat the pests and pesky things in life!

Simply count your blessings, focus on what's most important, and ask others—both humans and God—for ideas.

Meow for now,

Clive

I am meticulous about grooming and staying clean...I bathe a few times a day!

26
TAKING CARE OF BUSINESS—
BEFORE IT'S TOO LATE

Taking out the trash. I don't let my "trash" pile up. If my parents don't get rid of my waste from my box in a timely manner, I take my "business" elsewhere. We have a deal—I go in my box, and they clean it. It's simple. If they don't keep their end of the bargain, they get to pick up my trash from someplace they don't think is a trash repository—like the carpet.

Daddy does his part to take out my trash—most of the time. He scoops my box because the smell of litter makes Mommy gag. He also takes out the bigger trash bag from the entire house. Mommy says it's a manly job, and Daddy doesn't mind.

Although Mommy isn't naturally as neat as Daddy and I are, she has learned that she functions best in a neater environment. She tries to straighten up her desk each day before she stops for the day.

Mommy also makes sure the dishes are cleaned after she and Daddy eat. I happily help her do the dishes by licking a plate if I'm given that opportunity to contribute!

Grooming myself. I not only like my "box" clean, but also, I like to keep my entire body clean. That's why I let Mommy get the gunk out of my eyes as I mentioned earlier. My eyes are one of the only places I can't clean on my own. Every morning after Mommy gets the eye gunk out, I take a bath, starting with my paws and face, and then I proceed to my entire body. It just makes me feel better and ready for my day. I also wash my paws and mouth after I eat by licking my paws.

Daddy had to help bathe me for a while. After we moved to the small country cottage that I talked about in my last musing, I got fleas! To get rid of those pesky pests required even more serious scrubbing than I could manage! Daddy would have to take me into the shower with him every day and wash me in his arms. I didn't mind it. He's my daddy, and he knows what's best! And after a few weeks, those itchy boogers were finally gone!

Staying fueled. I never have a problem with taking care of the "business" of fueling up! I LOVE MY FOODIE, and I eat each morning to get me going. I also love to re-fuel at the end of the day at dinner time. Eating twice a day gives me plenty of energy for loving my humans as they get ready, for inspiring my mommy to write during the day, and for greeting my Daddy after he comes home each evening. Mommy and Daddy know it's best to stay fueled too. Mommy and Daddy both used to work through lunch, but they have since learned to take a break in the middle of the work day. All of us drink water any time we need to so that we stay hydrated. We especially need extra water in the winter when both our human and feline skin gets dry and flaky.

Tackling hard issues. Mommy says it's best to address any difficult issues between humans before they get worse. She says she wishes that she could ignore these dif-ficulties—just like some felines ignore humans at times. Handling these conflicts, which are generally misunderstandings, rather than someone trying to be difficult, helps keep Mommy and Daddy healthy emotionally. Just like with emotional strug-gles, Mommy and Daddy believe in staying on top of physical challenges with their bodies. They try to eat well and exercise for maintenance, and they go the chiroprac-tor and get medical screening tests when necessary to ensure all is well. Mommy says that taking care of herself is her best strategy to ensure the highest productivity. I think she's so smart—and I am just like her!

I naturally do what's best for me because we felines are instinctual. Mommy says it can be harder for humans who have the ability to make choices rationally. She also says people asking others for accountability is a great way to help ensure that they take action. She says that all humans are all works in progress, and that all of them have room to grow.

So, allow me to ask you a few questions so you can be more like me, taking care of "business"...

What About You?

- Are you doing your best to take care of "business" in everything you do?

- Are there ways that you can improve how you deal with clutter to help your organization skills at home or work?

- Is there one thing you can focus on to improve your health or life?

- Is there a conversation you need to have?

That's enough of me asking you questions! Let me go back to taking care of my own "business"—time for another bath, and then…another nap!

Meow for now,

Clive

Sitting in one of my attractive poses, looking upward, as I often do...

27

KEEPING MY EYES FOCUSED UPWARD

After we got settled into our country cottage, I adjusted, and life went back to normal… until I had a new challenge and began…

Fearing a new situation. One time, my parents took me to their friends' house to help care for another cat. From the beginning of this adventure, I was scared.

Watching my parents pack was scary because I knew they were going to leave, but then I was relieved for a moment when they took me with them. Riding in a car was also scary because I was inside the moving monsters that I often see from the window. When Mommy decided to hold me outside of my cage in her lap, though, I calmed down. As I've told you before, being in one of my human's laps makes everything better. However, I got scared again when I was put back into the cage and carried into a strange new house. I began…

Vocalizing anguish. I let my parents know—under no uncertain terms—that I didn't like this situation with my deep howls and hair standing up on end. But none of the previous events were as scary as encountering a fluffy white creature with green eyes once the door of the new home was opened and my cage was set down on the floor.

Would my parents love him more than me? Why were they petting him? I hissed at this creature through my cage and roared at him with a growl 10 times deeper than the ones I had uttered up to this point. I then started…

Observing a different reaction. The creature—I heard my parents call him Ivan— wasn't looking at me. In fact, he wasn't flinching at all. He just kept looking up as my daddy bent down to pet him. Ivan stood up on his hind legs to get more pets from my daddy's hand. I was clearly...

Lacking understanding. I howled even louder when I continued to see MY DADDY pet this creature! *How could this white fluff ball not even be looking at me—and be in so much peace as if nothing was upsetting him—when I was in so much duress? And when would my Daddy stop petting him?*

I couldn't understand why Ivan wasn't scared since I was. My daddy walked away, and Ivan stopped looking up. Then, in an instant, Ivan's demeanor changed. Ivan looked around on his own level. He saw me. He saw my mouth moving. And Ivan's peace vanished. He realized there was an enemy in his house.

Ivan, keeping his yes focused upward, unaware of me, a foreign feline in his home...

I learned later that Ivan is deaf, which is why he didn't get upset as I screamed and why he initially didn't see me. Being deaf also caused him to be more attentive to humans than some cats are since he has to rely on humans more to be safeguarded from danger. That attentiveness has trained him to keep his eyes on humans when they are near him. That's why his eyes were focused on my daddy. Ivan relied on...

Intervening protection from above. Despite Ivan's fear and potential vulnerability with his hearing handicap, Ivan wasn't in any danger from me. I was caged. I couldn't hurt him—and he couldn't hurt me. My humans kept us separated the entire time. In so doing, they kept us both safe. I am always amazed that my humans are so protective of me, and that they always know what to do. I am so thankful to have them!

Mommy says that she and Daddy aren't the only ones who protect from above. She says that Big Daddy (God) does that too. She says Big Daddy tells us to look up too, especially when we don't understand. Big Daddy, in His book says, "Set your mind on things above, not on things on the earth" (Colossians 3:2, NKJV). I try to remind myself of that, and I look up—a lot!

I was also thinking about how Ivan couldn't hear something at his own level. That shows me that sometimes Big Daddy keeps us from seeing the entirety of the situation for our own protection. Other times, we may be aware of the dangers, and Big Daddy gives us peace in the midst of the challenges. He says in His book that "Keeping our eyes on Jesus, the champion who initiates and perfects our faith" (Hebrews 12:2, NLT) is a good idea.

What About You?
Do you ever get scared when you encounter something new? Do you complain in protest like I did? Mommy says humans might face these fears, especially in situations that can be difficult, like when they have to go to a doctor, when they need to move because of a job transfer, or if they need to speak in public.

Are you facing new, scary, or overwhelming scenarios? What has your reaction been so far? Are you at peace or are you grumbling in dismay?

If you are growling internally, or even out loud like I did at Ivan's, consider a different reaction. Look up and focus on things above—and trust that Big Daddy knows what's best.

Ask Him for wisdom and to lessen your anxiety. He will get you through the situation and make you stronger in the process.

Meow for now,

Clive

Collaborating with Mommy, sitting at her computer.

28
I'm a Collaborative Coworker

As I've told you, Mommy has worked from home for many years. I remember getting excited when there started to be voices coming from the screen. I would go say "mrow" (hi) whenever I heard humans—or animals.

Mommy started teaching online writing classes in 2018, so the voices coming from the screen became more frequent. Today, in 2022, she is typing my words, and I am watching her. I heard voices coming from her online writing group, so I had to make sure I said "mrow" to them before I laid down and took a nap. She needs other humans to collaborate with, just like I need her to type my words. Being collaborative is the way to go, as Mommy and I are learning…

My absolute favorite time to make my presence known online is when I see other animals on the screen. Then I definitely have to say "mrow" to them. I also am a little competitive, so I have to make sure all the humans on the screen love me the most. I know I usually can't win over the owner of the other animal, but I can usually charm everyone else ☺.

Mom enjoys when I collaborate with her by lying at her feet because I give her inspiration for writing—I'm really smart, and as you may be able to tell, she can read my mind SO well!

I also love being a collaborative coworker because I don't really have to work much. Mine is more of a supporting role. As I may have let on, sometimes Mommy says I'm an angel in disguise…

(Don't tell her she's right—I can't let her in on all my secrets!)

I will sit in Mommy's lap when she is at her desk if she puts me there, but I am so long that I hang off on one side. She can't type sitting at her desk and pet me at the same time, so if she's not going to pet me, I'd rather move to a nearby bed or couch to take a nap.

Mommy tells me that the noises I make when I sleep are peaceful and help make her happy. Every once in a while, when she takes a break, she comes and gives me a "mamma smash"—which is kind of like a "mamma sandwich" except she generally doesn't lie down with me, she just bends over at the waist and leans her head on mine. Whatever affection she offers, I purr with delight and lick her finger.

Then she goes back to work, and I go back to sleep...I have a great life! If Daddy is home, I get to be a collaborative coworker with him, too. His work chair is wider than mommy's, so it's easier for me to get up on his lap when he's sitting in his chair than it is for me to get on mommy's lap. Although supporting them in their work isn't difficult, I think I have a bigger job to help make humans love my species. Like any species, some of us aren't nice. But my breed is… tabbies are loving and easy going. I sleep through (most of) the night, and I behave myself. Mommy says that when I go to Heaven, she will likely get another one of my kind. But, since my kind can live to be 20, we both hope I'll get to be here for a while! She still has much to write, so my work here isn't done, yet—unless Big Daddy says so!

What About You?

What lessons are you learning as you collaborate with others? Do you have others that you regularly learn from? How do others make you better? Are you facing challenges with other humans? If so, ask Big Daddy for help so that your collaborative efforts are successful and efficient. He tells us in His Word that…

> In the abundance of [wise and godly] counselors there is victory (Proverbs 11:14, AMP).

So, I guess Big Daddy wants us to have numerous counselors and people to collaborate with. That's fine by me! I love people, so I think this plan is a good one—especially if each one of them gives me foodie! I LOVE MY FOODIE!

Meow for now,

Clive

Burrowing my face in my favorite blanket—the one that is both fuzzy and that has pictures of my mommy and daddy!

29
LOVING THINGS THAT REMIND ME OF THE PEOPLE I LOVE

I love fuzzy blankets. I love the texture of them. I love the softness against my face and skin. What do I love even more than fuzzy blankets? My Mommy and Daddy! So, what is my favorite fuzzy blanket? It's a fuzzy blanket that has my humans' names on it, along with pictures of them at their wedding, in front of a waterfall, at a beach, and at a concert. My daddy gave this special blanket to my mommy for Valentine's Day one year.

Most afternoons, if you looked for me at my house, you would find me cuddled up on this blanket, dreaming. As you can see by my picture, I burrow my face into the blanket. Seeing Mommy and Daddy's faces comforts me and makes me excited for the next time I might lie on top of one of their chests.

I'm not the only one who appreciates photographs and the memories associated with them in my household. My mommy and daddy appreciate them too! As I've told you, my mommy has my picture as a kitten on the fridge, and she has a couple other photographs of her happily holding me in other parts of the house.

Whenever Mommy has people over, they always see me in the various photos. They comment on how cute I am. I hear voices, and then I make my grand entrance, flopping down in front of our guest's feet. I especially do this when one of my humans and a guest are standing by the fridge. I always hope that our houseguest will be overtaken with my cuteness, and then he or she will want to give me food.

There I go, talking about food again. It seems to always be the center of my thoughts. I LOVE MY FOODIE!

Get back to the point, Clive! Okay, okay, where was I?

Oh yes. Loving items in our home...

One particularly special, loving place where I often find Daddy's lap is in an old wooden rocking chair. Daddy loves sitting there because it reminds him of his loving mommy, who is already in Heaven. Near the rocking chair, we have another thing Daddy loves: a picture of a farm that his parents had in their house when he was growing up. The art depicts a young boy learning about making things. Sitting in this chair and looking at this painting reminds my daddy of what he loved as a boy. I'm glad Daddy is rediscovering who he was created to be: someone who makes things. He has started a business doing his passion—woodworking and making beautiful art, furniture, and chainsaw carvings. He said he may even make a carving of me one day! Mommy said she would love that! Daddy may even carve other people's fur babies too!

My point is that looking at sentimental things sparks ideas. You might want to make things for your enjoyment, for the enjoyment of people you love, or for the enjoyment of humans you don't even know. Mommy says that Big Daddy is the one who puts the feelings in humans to first have loving memories and then gives them inspiration to perhaps turn their memories or passions into creative items that bless themselves or others. Mommy believes that Big Daddy actually sent me so that she would be able to bless other animal lovers with my humor and insights. But that's enough about us...It's time that I ask...

What About You?

Do you have things that you love that remind you of people you love? A treasured photograph? A sentimental piece of furniture? A favorite book?

Or, who knows, maybe reading this book will inspire you to write or create something that Big Daddy has put in your heart.

And perhaps whatever you create will be the thing that someone else loves for years in the future because it reminds them of you.

Meow for now,

Clive

A kiss and a "mamma sandwich!"
How did I get so blessed?

30
MORE ABOUT THE "PARENT SANDWICH"

Do you have times when you feel the most comfortable? For me, that time is in the arms of both of my humans—literally in between their arms. Like I've told you, we call that a "parent sandwich." I get pets or snuggles from both of them this way. I let them know I love this activity by letting out my best purr, which is actually a "purr" followed by a "ppphhuu" sound I make with my mouth. My parents call it a purr snort—and it's a fabulous noise, if I do say so myself!

Now that I've talked about what I do—which is the most important thing for you to know—I can tell you more about the circumstances of the "parent sandwich." I always get this "sandwich" any time one or both of parents walks in the door, as long as the other parent is nearby.

If Mommy is already home, and we are welcoming Daddy home, I usually beat MOMMY to greet him because I run, unless I am really deep in a cat dream. When Daddy picks me up, Mommy snuggles both me and Daddy. He will then kiss her above my head. As they kiss, it naturally makes our beloved "parent sandwich." After they have kissed each other for a bit, Mommy snuggles her head onto my head, which I also love. I rub my head on her too! After all the head rubbing is through, Mommy begins to talk with Daddy about his day.

After they chat briefly, and I listen, I ask them for a "welcome home" treat. If it's a normal day when Mommy has been working from home and Daddy is just getting home around 5 or 5:30 p.m., I have to wait until 6:30 p.m. for my dinner. I normally don't get a treat that close to dinner. If it's not a normal day, though, and they have been gone for a few days, they will for sure give me a "welcome home" snack. Because I sometimes get this extra treat, I ALWAYS ask for it with a fervent meow. I LOVE MY FOODIE!

When my humans have been gone for a while, after the "parent sandwich" and my "welcome home" snack, I need more love. I need to make up for lost time—and I want them to know that. So, next, whenever they sit or lie down, I jump up on the bed or the couch near them. I lie down and look at them with longing.

What comes next is another type of "parent sandwich" that we also call the "smash." I mentioned it before. In this "sandwich," one of my parents is standing on one side of the bed. First, Mommy or Daddy will bend over and put his or her head down near mine. Then either he or she will pet me with one hand and put the other arm around me. They don't put all their weight on me. They are usually supporting most of their own body weight some other way.

My humans know me, and they know what I like and what I don't like!

Whatever kind of "parent sandwich" they give me, I meow with delight. I am SO happy to be in their arms again. How long I want this loving "parent sandwich" depends on how long it's been since I've seen them. If they were gone for more hours, I want a longer "sandwich." If they have been gone less than that, a shorter "sandwich" will suffice.

I have one more type of "parent sandwich"—it's when my Mommy or Daddy lie down. Each night before they fall asleep, I climb on their chests, effectively making the top piece of bread in the "sandwich." We also call this type of "sandwich" the "family pile." Either Mommy or Daddy is in the middle, and the bed is on the bottom. I stay on a chest for a while, rubbing my head against their hands asking for more pets. I also sniff Daddy's beard or lick his nose. Sometimes Mommy will also turn over and "sandwich" me between her and Daddy.

After a few minutes of being on a chest, I move to my human's feet. I try to go to Daddy's feet sometimes, but he always puts me on Mommy's feet. I fall asleep there most nights, and I start to have sweet cat dreams once again.

What About You?

Do you have a loved one (or a pet) who comforts you like I comfort my humans? If not, I know God loves you the way my humans love me. I know my humans will never run out of head scratches for me, and Mommy says Big Daddy will never run out of loving words and actions for you. He is the God of infinite, never ending love—and He always wants your love.

In fact, just like my humans look for me if I don't come looking for them, God comes to look for all His humans to. He wants to embrace humans in a "sandwich" of His love. If you are open and willing, you might come to love this kind of "sandwich" as much as I love my "parent sandwich."

Meow for now,

Clive

I love getting into Mommy's special baskets, which make unique nooks.

31
EXPLORING
NOOKS AND CRANNIES

After I have sufficiently loved on Mommy until about mid-morning, I start to seek a new adventure. I go exploring in all the nooks and crannies in our home. I start with under the table. I love scratching my paws against the area rug to show off my manliness. Even though my first human had me declawed as a baby, I still work to strengthen my bulging biceps.

I also love going under the couch bed. I get under the covers, but I still peek out… at least with my paws, Iike I'm doing in this photo.

What's so attractive about exploring a nook or getting into a cranny?

- I like to squeeze my body into spaces or boxes that are just my size to challenge myself to see if I can do it. After all, a dog couldn't get that small!

- I like to peek out without anybody knowing where I am.

- I like a change of scenery.

- I like to pretend that I can escape to another world.

- I like a cozy place to take a snooze.

- I like how a nook makes me feel safe and protected.

I know that my humans have the same affinity for nooks and crannies that I do. Sometimes, when they go on their own adventures, they check out the nooks and crannies in nature by hiking to unique rock formations in mountainous or hilly areas. You can read about those adventures on their blog, *Hiking With Your Honey.*

No matter how much I like being in nooks and crannies, I long to return to wherever my humans are. I may be unlike other cats because I want to be around people. But to me, the love and affection from Mommy and Daddy is better than hanging out by myself any day.

I get to spend much of my day with my mommy in one of the nooks where she works. These set-off-to-the-side places help her to not be distracted by the cares of home life. One of her nooks is a small corner desk in the guest room, and the other is a desk that Daddy built for her that fits in a bay window.

My favorite nook in the house is one my mommy created. At one end of the dining room, she placed two chairs in front of the fireplace, facing it. This arrangement makes a mini room. This nook is my favorite because Mommy, Daddy, and I spend much time there—it's a no-work zone. In the winter months, we also love to watch and listen to the fire in the fireplace.

Mommy will often go to this nook each morning before work to seek Big Daddy (God). He meets her there. She tells me that Big Daddy has a special "secret place," where He will dwell with all his children. His book (the Bible) says,

> He who dwells in the secret place of the Most High shall abide under
> the shadow of the Almighty (Psalm 91:1, NKJV).

Mommy says in this secret place, Big Daddy gives her peace, shows her ways to solve problems, tells her what to write each day, and provides guidance for her future. She even says that in this secret place, He gives her treats of love with words that delight her heart.

When she told me about "treats" in her secret place, I started going there too, hoping to get some treats because I LOVE MY FOODIE! I soon learned she didn't mean foodie treats, but Mommy still loves being in that nook…

What About You?
Have you explored a nook or cranny lately? Perhaps a change of scenery could be just what you need to get a different perspective to help you overcome a challenging obstacle. Perhaps a brain-break or a little snooze would help. Perhaps you would benefit from meeting with Big Daddy in His secret place…

He has hope, direction, and special treats waiting for you too!

CLIVE THE CAT CHIMES IN

Meow for now,

Clive

Peeking out of an under-the-bed "nook."

Once Mommy is settled in on the couch, I often reach out and hug her leg, like I'm doing here. 🐱

32

REACHING UP OR OUT FOR A RELATIONSHIP

When my humans get home, nine out of 10 times, they give me a "parent sandwich." Sometimes, however, our "sandwich" is delayed. Sometimes they are busy, or their arms are full. If that happens, I rub up against their legs. I try to be patient, but I can only wait so long.

If they are still standing at the door but they haven't yet picked me up, then I try my next tactic…I stand on my hind legs, and I rub their legs with my front paws. That action always gets their attention. They stop what they are doing and either pet me or pick me up.

I've learned that reaching up or out to get close when you don't feel close is a good solution. In fact, Mommy says that humans would be wise to follow my lead by reaching out to others if they feel distant from one another.

She admits that humans are too busy. Often, they don't notice others as much as they would like to in the middle of work or taking care of life. Mommy says that instead of getting mad at others who don't notice you right away, start reaching toward them. But she says that before you decide to reach out, you might also want to be more like me, and reach "up."

Many times, when Mommy looks up, she is praying. God comforts her because she knows that He ALWAYS sees her—even when others don't. She finds love and affirmation from the One who never disappoints, overlooks, or is too preoccupied for conversation. As she has learned to go to Him first, she has become a more patient person.

If Mommy is feeling ignored in some way, she asks God to give her empathy for others in their situations instead of immediately assuming that she is unimportant to them. Sometimes humans are just overwhelmed, busy, or perhaps they are depressed. Perhaps they don't want others to see their pain.

Mommy then asks God for the right opportunity to interact with others. She might send a text saying that she cares, asking if they would like to talk. Or she might reach out and say, "I know you are busy...don't feel the need to respond. Just know that I am here."

She does her part—whatever God tells her to do, and then she leaves the results up to Him. If the humans she reaches out to are unable to reach back, she will ask God to provide others to fill her desire for friendship. He always has the best answers.

More often than not, the human not answering my mommy is simply busy. Within a few days, an answer comes back, and it is usually one that pleases her. If there is no answer, Mommy has learned to see the lack of a response as God's protection.

There have been a few times out of hundreds—or even thousands—when God has told Mommy to no longer reach out to a person who is overly difficult. "Life is too short to be treated badly consistently," Mommy says. She's so smart—and I'm just like her 😊!

I'm NOT saying that we should stop interacting as soon as someone does something we don't like. We all "prick" each other sometimes, but our God, who models love, calls us to forgive one another. But if a pattern of hurt repeats more than a few times after you have talked to the person who pricked you, you may have decisions to make. If the other person shows no remorse, or if they are not living up to what they have promised, it could be time to set a distance or frequency boundary. Mommy says if we allow God to show us how to forgive, He will also show us what level of interaction is best.

Sometimes in this social media age of blocking others who we disagree with, it may be tempting to cut off relationships too soon. So, I'll say it again...Don't have less interaction with someone you care about because of a prick or two.

If Mommy and Daddy got rid of me or each other at the first prick, we would have missed out on the amazing times of love, laughter, companionship, and joy that we would have had as a family.

When Mommy and Daddy are at odds with each other, they look up to God and pray. Mommy and Daddy know that because they are husband and wife, God wants them to love each other for a lifetime. They are living out His words to "Love one another deeply, from the heart" (1 Peter 1:22–23, NIV).

They first ask God to help them practice forgiveness. Then Mommy asks Him to help her know what she can do to encourage and respect Daddy. Daddy asks God what he can do to make Mommy feel safe and loved.

As I've said, just like I reach up my humans' legs, Mommy and Daddy reach up to God in various ways. They reach to Him in prayer for help. But they also reach up to Him with their arms in praise. They have found that when they declare His goodness, their problems seem to get smaller. When they look up seeking direction, they often find the peace they need to move forward. Or perhaps they hear an encouraging word that makes them know that He sees their pain and will help them through it.

What About You?

Are you struggling in a relationship, friendship, or in communication with others in any way right now? If so, Mommy and I encourage you to reach up for help from God before you share any hurts or misunderstanding. As you reach up, we encourage you to ask Him how you might approach these delicate situations in a way that honors Him and is best for you and the other human involved.

God sees humans with compassion and gives them wisdom. We are confident that He will either improve your situation, remove you from it, or give you peace to walk through the difficulties.

It's time for me to reach up for my parents and, once again, demonstrate that I'm willing to go higher to give and receive their love.

Meow for now,

Clive

Resting with Daddy after he reads about one of Big Daddy's healing powers—rest!

33

ONE OF BIG DADDY'S HEALING POWERS—REST

One thing that we as cats have down better than humans is getting enough rest. As I've mentioned a few times, and you likely know, we cats take naps anytime we need them. My humans are getting better at resting when they need it, but they haven't always been that way.

My humans both tell stories of when they didn't heed physical exhaustion cues. They either got sick, angry, or had adverse circumstances. They have learned to listen to their bodies instead of running toward burn out.

They have also learned that Big Daddy heals in many ways— and rest is one of His main instruments. In fact, as you may know, Big Daddy wrote about rest in His "top 10" list. He uses a fancy word, "sabbath," but what that means is to take a day to rest. If Big Daddy wrote about rest in His "top 10" list, rest must be important to Him!

I am a cat; I rest most days. Humans are bigger and stronger than me, so it would seem that they would need more rest than I do to restore their bigger bodies. But in general, I believe that humans rest far less than felines. I also think most of them need more rest than they are actually getting. Because I love my humans, I remind them to rest with the best method—modeling. I take my cat naps where they can see me!

But this musing is supposed to be about Big Daddy and how He heals—not about what I do, so let me get back to Him.

Another way Big Daddy heals is through His Book, the Bible, and through other books about Him. My humans have been on a journey toward emotional healing since I have known them. Mommy says humans may get in physical fights (like cat fights when they bite or scratch or swat each other), but most often, they accidentally hurt each other emotionally. Also, Mommy and Daddy talk about the "fallen world"—a fancy way to say that the world is messed up. I know the world is "fallen" because I don't get to eat the amount of food that I want—and that's messed up!

Isn't everything about food? No? But I LOVE MY FOODIE! Hold on a minute: "Where's my foodie, Mommy?"

She told me I have to stick to the topic and finish this musing before I get a snack, so let's see…*where was I?*

Oh yes, I remember now. I was talking about the world being hard. As I said, one way my humans try to cope with life's challenges is to read uplifting books about Big Daddy. Often, as I have told you about, they read the Bible in the morning, and then they read books by others, sometimes about healing, at night. On weekends, they may also read in the middle of the day. Books do the trick in helping my parents rest. They often fall asleep reading them—even when they are interested in the subject matter. My humans falling asleep isn't a reflection on the quality of the book—it's because they are tired, and books help them relax.

I hope this book is helping you relax!

I give you permission to stop reading my book. Go take a nap—I mean it!

I'm not sure you took a nap…or maybe you did.

Anyway, in case you want to keep reading, I'll keep going on my musing—a snack awaits!

I want to encourage you to allow Big Daddy to use one of His most powerful tools—rest—as a healing tool for you. If you are like Mommy and Daddy, you will fight less with others if you apply God's healing power of rest.

So go rest! Unless you just woke up, or unless you are too lazy. Then you might need to get up and move ☺. I don't advise that humans become as lazy as some of us larger felines…

If I could bet, I would get rich in wagering that there are more humans reading this book who need more rest than those who are lazy. After all, lazy people don't read much!

Sometimes I amaze myself at my smarts…but then Big Daddy reminds me not to get prideful. I have to remain a cat angel rather than cop a catitude…

What About You?

Do you habitually get enough rest?

Do you ever feel like your mind is "spinning"?

Do you find yourself having restless nights?

As I've mentioned elsewhere, Mommy and Daddy say the best way to rest is to ask Big Daddy for help. Daddy wanted a tangible reminder for Mommy to ask Big Daddy for help with rest at night—so he bought her a large pillow with the following words from Big Daddy's book:

> Now because of you, Lord, I will lie down in peace and sleep comes
> at once, for no matter what happens, I will live unafraid!
> (Psalm 4:8, TPT).

If either of them is having trouble clearing their minds to rest, they read those verses out loud. I invite you to read them at night too…

Rest well, humans!

Meow for now,

Clive

Looking cute in a bed is just part of my routine!

34

ROUTINES AND RESETTING MYSELF

As a cat, I have a built-in clock. When my humans moved into the house where we live now, and Daddy was leaving early for work to beat the morning traffic, they started going to bed at 8 p.m. and getting up at 4 a.m. I follow them everywhere and do what they do, so that became my schedule too.

I am always on their bed ready to sleep at night. Sometimes, if they aren't there with me, I get frustrated and try to corral them. Sometimes they don't listen. Especially lately. They are talking about many things later than normal.

Once they do lie down, we have a bedtime ritual. Before I can go to sleep, I lie on Daddy's chest, and Mommy snuggles us. This arrangement, as I have mentioned, is what we call the "family pile." Daddy then puts me on Mommy's feet to sleep. Me being on Mommy's feet comforts her, so that's where I stay for quite a while. Many times, I even fall asleep there. If Mommy kicks me during the night, I may move.

No matter what time they go to bed, I get on top of Mommy's chest or back or side if she isn't up by 4:30 a.m. She then goes to the potty, and I lay on her feet there. As I've said, (but it's been a while, and I don't want you to forget)—I LOVE LYING ON FEET WHEN ONE OF MY HUMANS IS ON THE POTTY.

After Mommy is done on the potty, she picks me up and takes me back to the bed where she side snuggles me. I purr with delight!

I don't get on top of Daddy, though, until after he wakes up. As I said before, he gives me a gentle "left foot of fellowship" if I wake him up. After Daddy is awake, he pats his hand twice on his chest, signaling he is inviting me to "come on up and lie down." If Daddy is snuggling Mommy, I get on top of both of them! Sometimes, Mommy snuggles Daddy in the middle of the night. That's the only time Daddy won't get mad at me in the middle of the night. Snuggling Mommy ALWAYS makes Daddy happy, no matter what time it is! He loves her so much—and so do I!

Sometimes, if my humans are not getting up, I go back to sleep too. But not too long! They are supposed to be up! I have to be their alarm clock, which I accomplish with a steady, strong series of meows!

I meow because my daddy must get up so that he has time to get me my early morning creamer treat! Daddy refills his coffee cup before he leaves so I usually get two tastes of creamer before my morning meal. I LOVE MY DADDY!

As I've said, I usually get my meal every day at 6:30 a.m. and 6:30 p.m., and I get kind of loud the last hour, but especially the last 15 minutes before my foodie comes. As I'm sure I've mentioned, my foodie comes out of a black box (my humans call it an automatic feeder), but I remind my humans that I'm on a schedule, just in case that thing doesn't work or in case they want to feed me early.

If we have other humans in our house, sometimes Mommy or Daddy feed me even earlier to keep me quiet so I don't wake the guests up at 4:30 a.m. Mommy and Daddy know that if one of them doesn't give me my foodie, I will go and meow in front of the guest room door.

I will do whatever it takes! I NEED MY FOODIE!

I love it when we have other human visitors…I like them, not just because I get my foodie early, but I like to show as many people as possible how cute I am. I do the "plop," which, as I've shared, is when I fall over onto my side, roll onto my back, and stretch my legs so that humans can see how long I am. I will also rub their legs. If they are sitting in a chair, I jump into their laps so that they don't have to reach down to pet me.

After all, I need to make sure that they come back…I want them to spend the night so I can get my FOODIE early again!

If we have guests and both Mommy and Daddy go back to sleep after they give me my foodie, I may go back to sleep with them. When my Daddy leaves, however, I cry at the door even if the guests are not awake, and they usually hear me. I get very upset when Daddy leaves. Mommy comes to comfort me, and when I realize I'm not alone, I calm down. Then it's time for me to go take a nap in the room with the morning sun.

In the afternoon, I usually go take a nap in my daddy's home office. I love it when he gets to work from home, but he isn't always there. My humans have an easier time finding me than I do them. I am more predictable than they are.

Could you humans be more predictable? My older cat brain is tired with all your changing routines!

If I'm too vocal, Mommy and Daddy have to scold me a bit to remind me that they set the routines. They change my food time twice a year when the time changes, and I adjust. They grab a hold of me and lie me down when they want to go back to sleep. If they haven't fed me, going back to sleep is hard. But, if I'm fed, and one of them keeps petting me, eventually I acquiesce. In other words, when I am provided for and have enough love, I eventually adjust to a new routine.

Mommy comforts me, because once again, she understands me. She says that she and Daddy have a larger brain than I do, and yet, they too get upset if their routine is changed.

At different times, new routines have come for my humans because of varying work project demands, a change of plans, a few days of visitors, an unplanned need to visit someone, or an unscheduled conversation. Mommy says that Big Daddy has, at times, someone or something else that He wants them to focus on other than me.

I also know, though, that I help my humans obey! They tell me that Big Daddy wants them to keep the discipline of routine whenever it's possible. He is a God of order. However, He gives them the ability to manage their own time as well.

When Mommy first became an entrepreneur with a flexible schedule, imposing this discipline was difficult for her. She tended to procrastinate when she would struggle with fear.

I understand why she may want to take lots of catnaps after hearing about some of her struggles, but God didn't create her that way.

She has a purpose to fulfill. She loves Big Daddy and does her best to do what He says.

Big Daddy is just like my daddy. Big Daddy sets His rules that are good for humans out of love, just like my daddy sets rules for me. Big Daddy also loves humans by giving them everything they need and by giving them choices. Also like my daddy, whose love never stops for me, Big Daddy's love never stops for them, no matter if my humans *see* Him working or not.

My humans tell me they think it is wise to follow Big Daddy around like I follow them around. They learned that lesson from Big Daddy's book, from words that say:

> You are to follow only GOD, your God, hold him in deep reverence, keep his commandments, listen obediently to what he says, serve him—hold on to him for dear life! (Deuteronomy 13:4, MSG).

And, if my humans don't know where Big Daddy is, I know He wants them to go look for Him, just Iike I go look for my humans if they aren't where they are supposed to be.

Ultimately, just like I am happier when I am near my humans, my humans are happier if they are near Big Daddy. Sometimes, just like me, they forget where they are most loved (in the company of Big Daddy), and they wander off and go somewhere on their own. And just like my humans come to find me if I've been gone too long, so Big Daddy goes to find them.

Don't you love all these parallels I see! I AM SO SMART! NO DUMB JOCK HERE—well, I'm not a jock, but I do run really fast when my feeder makes noise and gives me foodie! I LOVE MY FOODIE!

What About You?
Do you have routines that help you out? Do you get upset if your routine changes? If your routine does change, what do you do to reset your expectations and find peace?

You likely have some pretty good methods, just like Mommy, Daddy, and I do. Today I'd like to end with a prayer of blessing from the Bible:

> May mercy and peace and love be multiplied to you [filling your heart with the spiritual well-being and serenity experienced by those who walk closely with God] (Jude 1:2, AMP).

CLIVE THE CAT CHIMES IN

Meow for now,

Clive

Me sitting on one of the many chairs in our living room where I amuse our guests.

35

MUSICAL CHAIRS

As I've said on multiple occasions, I like to be everywhere my humans are. In the wintertime, my humans are cozied up in a lovely nook that I've mentioned before with two chairs fairly close to the wood-burning fireplace.

Daddy loves to chop wood from the yard to build our fires. As soon as Daddy is done building the fire, he sits in his chair near the fireplace, and I jump on his lap. Every now and then, he gets up to put more wood on the fire. When he does that, I have to get up so that he can get up. I love it when he gets up because…

Now his chair is mine! *Yay!* But then he comes back and moves me into his lap again. A little later, he gets up again to make a hot beverage or to go to his "box" (that's the loo or potty in case you forgot).

Then I get his chair again! *Another yay!* Sometimes he isn't gone for more than a minute, and we play this game of me repeatedly taking his chair and him repeatedly moving me into his lap. I think that at some point Daddy is going to get frustrated and let me have his chair, but he usually doesn't just let me have it if there is a fire in the fireplace that he needs to tend.

Here's another fun fact about our game…Despite Daddy beginning to sit down, I don't move. He acts as if he is going to sit on me, but I know he won't. One time he acted like he was going to put his weight on me, but he didn't. Usually, Daddy starts to sit but stops short of completely sitting completely down, turns around, grabs me, and helps me resettle on his lap. Even though I don't get his chair to myself, I am still happy because I love his lap.

When we are all settled in our chairs, Mommy and Daddy talk, or they take turns reading a book. I listen and purr for as long as Daddy is seated. Sometimes I even go to sleep with him! Here's a picture of both of us sleeping on his chair! I am just like my daddy!

Taking a snooze, just like Daddy does in his favorite chair!

Another place we play musical chairs is in the kitchen. Whenever Mommy gets up to get something else for the table at mealtime, I get in her chair, and I sit up and look at what's on the table. I know I can't get on the table, but if I look innocent and courteous, maybe they will give me something. When she comes back, she has to push me out of her chair because I resist with all of my burley 23 pounds! I usually don't get between Daddy and his foodie, because if I do, I will get in trouble. If Mommy gets up again, I get in her chair again, though!

One day, after a couple rounds of this game, Mommy got smart. She moved me to my own chair. I like to be on my humans' level so they can see me constantly. I've learned to stay in my chair after they put me there. They look at me periodically as they eat, and if I continue behaving well, they will give me a plate or two to lick at the end of dinner.

A third time we play musical chairs is in our living room, when Mommy and Daddy are watching a movie or hanging out with friends.

When it's just Mommy and Daddy, they sit on the couch. I walk up to their legs and give them a cue that I am going to jump on their laps by looking at them. They know I'm happiest if they move together so there is no space between their legs. Then I can sit on both of them. They understand this preference, and they move together to indulge me.

When I get hot, I move. Sometimes, if there are more people sitting in the other chairs, I go up to everyone and rub against their legs to welcome them to the room. They usually pet me. Even people who don't like cats love me. I am a special cat! The more pets I can get, the happier I am!

After I've said hi to everyone, I go sit in my own chair. Mommy has LOTS of chairs in that room. I sit up like a person so everyone can see how pretty my tummy is. I look at the people as they talk, moving my head to the person who is talking. They look back at me, so I know they are talking about how amazing I am!

I want everyone to know that I am a clean cat and well groomed, so I usually take a bath for everyone to see. Then, I clip my back toenails. I don't have any front claws. This act is loud, and I guess the sound is funny to humans because they generally start laughing and looking at me. I pause momentarily to look back at them, but then I get back to the business at hand (or paw)—a distinguished cat has to be well-groomed!

I stay in the living room until everyone gets up or it is our bedtime, whichever comes first. If it is bedtime, and my humans don't come, I start to go to the bedroom by myself, trying to lead them to follow. Someone in this house has to stay on schedule!

I meow loudly at my humans to try to convince them to come with me. Sometimes I am successful at persuading them, and sometimes I am not. After a couple of my best corralling meows, if they don't come, I go to bed by myself. I eventually get tired of waiting for them, and I fall asleep on their bed, dreaming of when they will join me.

Mommy and Daddy are not late-night people, so I don't usually have to wait for long. Sometimes I lay in the center of the bed if I want them to hug me, and I fall asleep. When Daddy gets there, he moves me to the foot of the bed to lie on Mommy's feet. I don't understand why I have to move when I get here first, but I love them, so it doesn't matter. I slip off quickly once again into dream land where there is more foodie or a treat to enjoy—and all is well. This talk about bedtime is making me tired. I better not forget to ask…

What About You?
Do you either play musical chairs or wear multiple hats at different points of the day or week? Perhaps you are both a daughter and a mother. Perhaps you are both an employee and the manager of a household. If playing different roles is fun for you, like a game of musical chairs, that's great!

If those different roles feel taxing or overwhelming, ask Big Daddy to help you prioritize your roles, or ask Him to give you ways to manage life in chunks of time.

Mommy says doing life in time blocks has worked wonders for her—so it may just help you too!

You can also ask Big Daddy for overall comfort if you feel overwhelmed. As the Psalmist (an-old time word for poet) says:

> When the cares of my heart are many, your (God's) consolations cheer my soul (Psalm 94:19, ESV, parenthetical addition added for clarity).

Meow for now,

Clive

36

CAPTURE YOUR THOUGHTS BEFORE YOU FALL ASLEEP

My mommy loves to journal. My daddy, after being married to Mommy for eight years, is also a fan of journaling. Writing in a journal helps humans remember their blessings, lessons, special events, and sentimental moments. A journal helps them converse with Big Daddy about things they are grateful for and things they are still asking Him for.

If I were to journal, I would record my days, even though they are fairly similar from one day to another. I've already told you about some of my activities, but my life is SO INTERESTING that I think it's fine to repeat them!

Therefore, if I could journal, I'd write things like:

- I got to have two tastes of creamer this morning from Daddy.

- My foodie was yummy, as always, this morning, and then I got to take a morning nap on Mommy's feet.

- I meowed at Mommy and the ladies on her screen.

- After my nap, I climbed on her lap, got Mommy to pet me, and laid down on the bed near where she writes.

- I got up again to go see Daddy at lunch and begged for food—unsuccessfully. I always beg anyway because I LOVE MY FOODIE—and I know that sometimes Daddy will give me treats!

My list would continue after Daddy leaves to go back to his woodshop in the afternoon.

- I take an afternoon nap on the fuzzy blanket with my humans' pictures on it so I can dream about being with them.

- At multiple points during the day, I go get some water and visit my "box" to get rid of that water.

My journal would go on to say...

- My mommy starts preparing dinner around 5 p.m., and that's when I start begging for my dinner.

- I don't get to eat until after they are done, which isn't fair. My food machine dispenses my food at 6:30 p.m.

- The vet says I can only eat twice a day, so that's why I get vocal...I am not a fan of the vet's weight loss plan! I LOVE MY FOODIE!

- I help my parents stay disciplined by reminding them to get to bed just after 8 p.m.

There you have it—I must really feel comfortable sharing my journal with you readers, who are complete strangers to me. I'm now tired after writing all that. Time for another nap...but let me not forget to converse with you, Dear Reader.

What About You?

Have you tried journaling yet?

In addition to blessings, lessons, and facts about your life, here are some questions you might consider asking yourself if you'd like to start journaling or capturing more of your thoughts in your journal:

- What decisions are currently weighing on you, and what are the pros and cons of your options?

- What are your goals and dreams?

- What prayers have been answered recently?

- Who are you still praying for and what are you asking God for on their behalf?

- What Bible verses are comforting to you? What verses don't you understand?

If you have journaled, Mommy and I encourage you to go back and read old journals. Or, if you are just starting now, we recommend you do this at a later time. If you are like us, you will be amazed by what has happened—and you may be surprised at how much you have forgotten.

We encourage you to do as the Psalmist did:

> "… I remember the days long ago. I reflect on all that you have done. I carefully consider what your hands have made. I stretch out my hands to you in prayer. (Psalm 143:5–6, NOG).

Meow for now,

Clive

Aren't open paws cute? In this case, I recommend following my visual example. 🐱

37

OPEN-PAWED:
READY TO RECEIVE

As I've told you before, I sit with my parents to pray. I do everything like them. Often, when they pray to Big Daddy, they turn their hands over to be facing up. I do it too as you can see by my picture.

This gesture signifies openness.

It also symbolizes the willingness to let go and not hold anything too tightly.

Big Daddy, through one of His poets, says in His book that He opens his "generous hand...full of blessings, satisfying the longings of every living thing" (Psalm 145:16, TPT).

Mommy and Daddy are created in Big Daddy's image, and the blessings they give me (food, water, my box, and lots of love) satisfy my longings too. Well, sometimes I beg for more treats—I CAN'T HELP MYSELF—I LOVE MY FOODIE!

I'm distracted from the flow of this musing now...*where was I?* Ah yes, open hands!

Sometimes open hands symbolize the touch of another. When Daddy or Mommy opens a hand face up, the other person knows that is an invitation to hold the other person's hand.

I see Mommy or Daddy open a hand as they pray sitting on the couch or as they get ready to ask God to bless their food.

So, I open my paws when I sit next to them sometimes too. This position shows them I am open to receive something; I even let one of them gently hold my paw.

Plus, this pose looks so adorable, don't you think? Mommy said her previous felines never did that with their paws…I'M A SPECIAL CAT!

Mommy also says that Big Daddy frequently prompts her to open her hands. She says sometimes she tends to clench her ideas or plans too tightly. Mommy has nails that poke her and cause her pain, though, if she clenches her hands for too long. She doesn't feel pain if her hands are open and relaxed. She reminds herself to keep her hands and heart open to however Big Daddy directs her. She knows Big Daddy has wonderful gifts in exchange for her openness. Mommy's open hands aren't just for Big Daddy. Mommy also reaches out to Daddy with open hands, so that Daddy knows that she wants his touch or his help.

As she is typing my words for this musing, Mommy is trying to have open hands, but she is a bit stressed to finish everything she needs to do before she and Daddy leave to go out of town to visit family.

I would be stressed because my humans are leaving our house for a week, but they have someone come and check on me every day because they know I don't like to be alone.

Big Daddy directed Mommy and me to this "Open Hands" subject this morning so that she would do her best and let him order her next steps—even if it all didn't get done. She said after we prayed, she realized she could do some of the tasks on the road as Daddy drives if need be.

So, today…me, Mommy, Daddy, and Big Daddy encourage you to pray the following prayer,

> *Lord, I let go of everything that stresses me. I surrender it all…take it all out of my hands. I ask that You symbolically place instead, in these hands, only what they need for this day. Place peace in these hands. Place comfort in these hands. Place love in these hands. Place abilities in these hands for whatever you want to be done today.*

Mommy tells me as she looks at her open hands that she is reminded of Big Brother's (Jesus') nail-scarred hands. He died on a cross with immense pain in His hands and throughout His body to make a way so that people could be comforted by the amazing never-ending love of the Father (Big Daddy). Jesus (Big Daddy's Son), by taking on the punishment the world deserved, enables us to receive forgiveness, love, and abundant blessing from the Father who is holy. Jesus enables a holy Father to only see us through His blood, which makes all of us acceptable in the Father's sight.

All we have to do to accept this free gift of receiving the sacrifice of Jesus is to acknowledge any known sin—ways in which we knowingly do the opposite of what would be pleasing to God. There are other types of sin too, but I'll leave that explanation to pastors and theologians. Or the Internet, if you'd like to learn more. Suffice it to say for this musing that the Bible says that "all have sinned and fallen short of the glory of God" (Romans 3:23). So, the reality is that we all need this free gift. If you are ready to receive this gift, simply bow your head in humility to demonstrate your acknowledgment of your need for God and open your hands to receive forgiveness in exchange.

I am just a cat, and I can't fathom the sacrifice Jesus made for humans, but I do know that my humans are grateful for His open hands, which enable them to open their hands to receive from Big Daddy.

I am also grateful for my humans' open hands. As I've told you before, I often rub my head in their hands or lick their fingers to show them how much I love their open hands—and then I place my paws in an upward, open position, too.

What About You?
We invite you to open your hands with us. Like us, you might be amazed what Big Daddy places there.

You might receive peace, like He brought my mommy today. You might receive some kind of material gift that suited a need you never thought would be possible. My humans received a monetary miracle from God in Fall 2021, which lifted a huge financial burden off their shoulders. Even if you don't receive an immediate gift, if you believe in Jesus, you will receive the gift of eternal life—the longest lasting and best gift of all…

Big Daddy has amazing gifts to offer! He wants to give gifts to those humans (and cats) with open hands.

Meow for now,

Clive

Loving my time with Daddy, shortly after I enjoyed a creamer treat that caused me to say, "mrr," which means thank you.

38
ALWAYS SAY "MRR"

My Daddy drinks A LOT of coffee. He is doing better though. He has moved from two pots of coffee a day to a few cups. I don't mind that he drinks coffee often, because whenever he drinks his coffee, he gives me creamer. When he opens the fridge to get the creamer out, I affirm his action by meowing. He has told me to be quiet and patient, and I am learning. Sometimes, though, I still cry with anticipation.

Right after he gives me my treat, I always change my tone, and I say, "mrr," which is "cat" for thank you. I'm happy to "mrr"…to affirm my daddy and to let him know that he did the right thing by giving me a treat. When I "mrr," he can tell that I appreciate him.

I want to do anything that makes Daddy happy. Even though I LOVE my creamer, I have learned to not ask Daddy for more, but instead, I have learned to be grateful that he gave me a snack. Appreciating what I have and not begging for more makes Daddy more apt to give me more on his next cup of coffee. If I love and appreciate his gift, he loves me right back. I used to be obnoxious, asking for more. He had to give me a few bops on the head until I learned to stop meowing after I enjoy one treat.

Daddy works hard to provide me food and treats, so I want to be grateful and appreciative instead of pesky.

I've heard Mommy say that gratitude is also integral to her relationship with Daddy and Big Daddy (God). I learned to say "mrr" from her. As I've told you, she says thank you to Big Daddy each morning by writing a letter to Him in her journal. She says one of the main verses that inspires her to praise Him each day is:

Praise the LORD for the glory that belongs to him. Worship the LORD because of his beauty and holiness (Psalm 29:2, NIRV).

She has a whole article about how she praises God in her writing on her blog. If you'd like to read it, go to https://loralpepoon.com/praise-precedes-all-my-writing/.

Mommy also says thank you often to Daddy for their date nights, for fixing things, for loving her when she is difficult and scared, and for how hard he works to provide for us. Mommy used to work in a stressful job, so she remembers how hard that is—and Daddy has done that for many years.

We are praying that someday soon Daddy can spend more time pursuing what he loves full time—woodworking. As I might have told you, he rediscovered his love for woodworking when he made Mommy a beautiful cedar desk that fits in the bay window where Mommy is writing right now.

I like to get on top of her desk and look out the window. I get up there to watch birds and Mommy and Daddy when they go out on the deck. I meow loudly at Mommy and Daddy to try to get them to come back in! When they are back inside, I always purr and let them know I'm grateful to see them by saying, "mrr."

Mommy tells me that sometimes humans are like I used to be—they say "more" more often than they say "mrr" (thank you) after a blessing. Their minds, like mine, are often on to the next thing before they express gratitude. But, Mommy says that the more people pause and say thank you each morning, the more they will automatically say thank you about more things.

What About You?
Do you say thank you to people you love as often as possible? When are the times that you like to hear someone say thank you to you? Could you say thank God more often? I know saying thank you more makes me and my humans happier, so I think it might make you happier too.

Time for me to say "mrr" to my amazing parents once again as I jump up on their laps for a snooze.

Meow for now,

Clive

I love my mommy and being held by her!

39

SEVEN WAYS
I AM LIKE MY MOMMY

When some humans are teenagers, some of them tend to say, "I will never be like my parents." After they have been an adult for a bit, say in their 30s and beyond, humans begin to realize how much they are like their parents. I'm well into cat adulthood, although it would be improper to divulge my age, so I'm not going to share that with you.

I'll just get to the point—I've noticed seven ways I am like my mommy. This musing is for you, Mommy!

1. **I love to be right up in my loved ones' space!** As I've said throughout this book, I'm so thankful for my Mommy and Daddy! I've mentioned how I show my love much of the time by sniffing faces, settling on laps, or lying on chests. I lie on Mommy's lap or on her chest often if she has her laptop. I see Mommy lie on Daddy's lap or chest, so I learned that trick from her! She's so smart—and I AM JUST LIKE HER! Like my Mommy, I can interrupt whatever is happening if I want love. My daddy can be working on his blog, which tells of their adventures together, and Mommy walks up to him, and sits or lies on his lap and asks, "What are you doing?" He is always kind to her—just like she is kind to me.

2. **I beg for food if I smell something good.** I also learned this behavior from my mommy. If Daddy has something on his plate that she wants, she will always ask him to share multiple times—until he gives in. And that's all I'm doing when I meow when my humans eat! If they don't give me any foodie after my first meow, I meow repeatedly. As I've said, I'm vocal and passionate! I LOVE MY FOODIE!

3. **I love gazing out the window on a beautiful day when the sun is shining.** I see Mommy look out the window longingly as she is waiting for the words to come that she writes. I watch her close her eyes and warm her face as the sunshine comes through the window. I do that too! After I glance at everything out the window—I lie on my back and just bask in the sunlight. That's why Mommy loves where we live now. We have beautiful views of trees and the sun and the woods, and three windows where she typically sits and types—or takes sun absorbing breaks.

4. **I love bird watching.** My daddy calls my mommy "bluebird queen" because she loves bluebirds, and because bluebirds played a part in her coming to Tennessee. But that's another story she will have to tell in a book about her life. I love watching the bluebirds, robins, cardinals, blackbirds, and any other bird I see outside. I meow at them quietly and wag my tail, but they don't seem to hear me.

5. **I go through many hair ties.** Mommy is always putting these things in her hair and taking her hair down again and leaving the hair tie wherever she is—and she thinks they disappear. As I've shared, hair ties are my absolute favorite toy. I take them. I chase them all over the floor until they go under a piece of furniture. But she doesn't see where they go, and I can't retrieve them once they are underneath something. Whenever we move next, we will find all the lost hair ties and have great fun with the abundance of these amazing toys!

6. **I am most content at home, but I long to get outside, too.** My mommy works at home, and she has to go run an errand just to get out sometimes so she can see the outside world. I totally get that. I want to get outside every time a door opens. I always get right to the door, but then one of my humans blocks me from getting out. Then I remember that they are in the house, and I am content to stay inside—because my number one priority is to be with them.

7. **I am comforted by talking to my people.** Mommy loves to talk to Daddy most of all, but she also loves to talk to my Gigi (her mommy) and her friends. She talks on the phone a few hours a week, or she leaves to go to see her friends. I prefer that she talk on the phone so I can still see her. I am like Mommy because I like to talk and respond. When Mommy feeds

me, I say, "mrr" (thank you). When she calls me, I perk up. When she calls my name and pats her lap or rubs her chest, I come. I know her signals for wanting love—and I'm happy to oblige. Once I get settled, I talk with loud purrs so she knows how comforted I am to be with her.

What About You?

Do you take after someone you love—like your parents? If you do and you're blessed to still have a parent on this side of Heaven, why not write how you are like him or her? As God says in the Bible:

> HONOR [esteem, value as precious] YOUR FATHER AND YOUR MOTHER [and be respectful to them]—THIS IS THE FIRST COMMANDMENT WITH A PROMISE—so that it may be well with you, AND THAT YOU MAY HAVE A LONG LIFE ON THE EARTH (Ephesians 6:1–3, AMP).

Mommy says if you write something that would be touching for you to read (if someone wrote those words about you), chances are the person you are writing about would enjoy receiving and reading it too!

It's time for me to stop writing and to go enjoy being with my mommy. Then it will be time for another cat nap...

Meow for now,

Clive

My best close-up photo, when
I'm poised to ask for more!

40

ASKING FOR MORE

Today is Sunday, and sometimes on a Sunday, my humans come home talking about what they learned at church. Today they were reminded that God delights in them as humans. God can't wait to give them good gifts, especially when they seek Him.

As they were talking about this message, Daddy made a concoction of coconut cream chocolate thickness. Daddy frequently experiments with sweet treats.

"Oh my, I have to give Clive some of this," Daddy said to Mommy.

My ears perked up, and I walked toward my treat bowl, eager to see what Daddy's new creation tasted like.

I hadn't done anything to earn this treat. Daddy's father's heart, out of love for me, just wanted to give it to me.

One taste, and I knew why!! I had a delicious bite, and I couldn't stop asking for more—it was so yummy!

Daddy only gave me a little bit more. He said he limited the quantity so I wouldn't get sick. But Daddy delighted in sharing something he loved with me! He's such a great Daddy!

Mommy chimed in as I wouldn't relent in meowing and asking for more. She asked: "How often are we relentless like Clive in asking God for more? Don't we more often say, "Oh, I just had a blessing—that's enough. And then we don't ask again."

Mommy is so insightful sometimes. I stare at her often as she talks. She is so smart! And, as I've said, I'M SO MUCH LIKE HER ☺.

Mommy kept going, as she said:

> I wonder if we let ourselves encounter God more often—tasting and seeing that God is good—as Psalm 34:8 instructs us to do, if we wouldn't then taste—more often—how amazing His gifts are. Perhaps we'd be 'pawing' and 'meowing' as we are begging for more of Him like Clive does to us.
>
> God says to "Ask…seek…knock" (Matthew 7:7). The tense there is present, meaning now and always now. God didn't say, 'Ask once a year.' Or if you asked before, He didn't say, "That's all you get." No, He wants us to eat our daily bread as He tells us in the Lord's Prayer.

I don't know about you, but I eat more than once a day! I LOVE MY FOODIE! So, I think God is okay with humans asking Him for things multiple times a day.

Mommy says that God calls humans to be grateful. Everyone wants to be appreciated, and humans are created in His image, so why wouldn't God want gratitude? But He also delights in taking care of every need for humans and animals.

Mommy believes that God delights in, not only taking care of us, but also, she says that He delights in sharing his most yummy treats with us—just like Daddy enjoyed sharing his new concoction with me. Sometimes those yummy treats aren't in the form of food, but I do know that somehow Daddy keeps discovering more yummy desserts and versions of interesting recipes! I'm so thankful that God made humans to be creative—and that He made Daddy to love sharing his treats with me! I LOVE MY FOODIE!

According to Mommy, God's "yummies" are also found in a hug or a snuggle, in the smell of flowers, or when the right amount of sunshine hits her face. Other "yummies" come in the form of sweet words. Or in a worship experience or finishing a creative project. Or maybe in an answer to a prayer…or even in a miracle.

Maybe the best "yummy," Mommy says, is just sitting in God's presence feeling His unconditional love. I see Mommy and Daddy's faces as they pray. They look so peaceful in prayer.

I will keep asking for more every time they have something yummy—for my palette and so that Mommy and Daddy are inspired to keep asking for more from God!

He created me to help, after all!

What About You?

Are you accustomed to asking God for more, often? Or do you tend to think that if you ask for something once in a while, you have likely already received your fair share? God has unlimited resources, and He is not stingy. On the contrary, He is super generous and abundant, as His book says in the following verse:

> Never doubt God's mighty power to work in you and accomplish all this. He will achieve infinitely more than your greatest request, your most unbelievable dream, and exceed your wildest imagination! He will outdo them all, for his miraculous power constantly energizes you (Ephesians 3:20, TPT).

I, for one, love this principle of being constantly energized. I have much eating, playing cute, and even more writing to do…

Meow for now,

Clive

41
CRYING OUT—FROM PERSISTENTLY TO PATIENTLY

I begin to cry PERSISTENTLY when I am hungry or when any kind of creamy treat is shared. As I've mentioned, my most common treats are a smidgeon of creamer or a few licks of creamy protein shakes. In eager anticipation, any time I see a carton come out of the fridge, or the blender makes noise, I cry for a treat.

As I've also said before, I cry for at least an hour before I get fed. Mommy picks me up and tries to distract me. Her petting me and loving on me calms me down, and I stop crying—for a bit.

Mommy was talking to Big Daddy one time, and He was trying to teach her a lesson using my behavior. He does that often, as you may be able to tell from reading this book! He knows she cares about me, and therefore, He know she may be more inclined to listen to Him when He is teaching her a lesson because of me! Big Daddy is so smart—and I'M CREATED BY HIM!

As I've shared, Mommy wonders sometimes if I'm an angel doing Big Daddy's work. I think Big Daddy just tells me what to do, and somehow, without even knowing He told me to do it, I do it. He does the work to speak to her. Anyway, here is what Mommy told me that Big Daddy said to her one time:

> *Be persistent in crying out for Me just as Clive is persistent when he is hungry. Cry out with the same intensity. Just as you can make Clive happy as he waits, I can do that for you. He doesn't know it is better for him to wait to eat…it is also better for you to wait for My answers, too.*

I can't make you understand why waiting is beneficial any more than you can make Clive understand why he needs to wait to eat. You, Loral, don't have the same level of understanding I do.

Your current level of limited understanding is not something you can do anything about—just as Clive can't do anything to increase his understanding. But I will give you revelation when you ask. I am working on the next miracle of your life the way your husband was a miracle for you. Do not doubt. How much more peace and security do you have than you did a year ago? I love you, child.

You are doing the right thing. Be a wife. Write. Share. Follow me each day. Exercise. Serve.

Although Big Daddy spoke these words to Mommy years ago, they could have been recorded this morning. They are every bit as true for her today as they were when she first heard them. Mommy says that the words Big Daddy gives her are for others too, so perhaps His words might be for you as well.

Mommy also says she has rarely met a person who is gifted in patience. Although she recently was discussing this musing with a friend who said she was blessed with patience. Mommy was surprised. But I think she's right that probably 95% of humans don't fall into the patient category.

That's why Big Daddy's book says:

> So let's not allow ourselves to get fatigued doing good. At the right time we will harvest a good crop if we don't give up, or quit. Right now, therefore, every time we get the chance, let us work for the benefit of all, starting with the people closest to us in the community of faith (Galatians 6:9, MSG).

Daddy was just quoting this verse to Mommy this morning to encourage her, because they are facing uncertainty as Daddy is entering a new world of work. He said Big Daddy wants them to know that all they have to do is:

Keep going. Keep doing what they know. Keep writing. Keep praying. Keep observing Big Daddy's lessons through Clive and other animals.

Sounds like pretty good advice.

Mommy, Daddy, and I are also grateful that Big Daddy doesn't mind when we repeatedly cry out to Him. After all, His book tells us to cry out to Him. The following verse is one of Mommy's favorites:

> "'Call to me and I will answer you. I'll tell you marvelous and wondrous things that you could never figure out on your own'" (Jeremiah 33:3, MSG).

Big Daddy promises to talk with humans—just like He does with my Mommy and Daddy. Mommy and Daddy don't always listen the first time when they are uncertain or scared, so I remind them about how Big Daddy is caring for them with another comforting message from His book:

> Cast all your worries on Him, for He cares for you. (1 Peter 5:7, TLV).

What About You?

Would you remember not to worry without multiple reminders? I know my parents have to comfort me multiple times a day—even multiple times an hour if it is the last hour before my foodie comes. I LOVE MY FOODIE!

Just like my humans comfort me, I am confident that Big Daddy will comfort you.

But don't take my word for it—I'm just a cat. Why not try crying out to Big Daddy for yourself?

Meow for now,

Clive

Relaxed and satisfied on one of my favorite furry blankets after my brilliant humans calmed me down once again.

42
UNCONTROLLABLE WAILING CEASES

As I've mentioned many, many times, when I'm hungry, I cry uncontrollably for food, pacing if Mommy or Daddy are doing something other than feeding me. Since Mommy and Daddy ration my food, I always have to ask for more. As you also know by now, I'm a 23-pound hunk-of-feline love—and I am well taken care of. I'm a big bear of a tabby with an appetite to match.

Despite my crying, Mommy or Daddy can get me to stop crying by snuggling me on a lap nestled on top of one of my favorite furry blankets. My cries quickly turn into purr snorts, and I pose proudly on my lap throne. My paws either kneed the blanket, or they are relaxed and crossed. And I roar my purr-motor.

Why the sudden shift from the deep stress of surely coming starvation to exemplifying my majestic prowess?

Because now when I go to sit on Mommy or Daddy's laps, I'm comforted by being there with them. I know I am unconditionally loved.

Mommy says watching this transformation ministers to her frustrated, pent-up, things-aren't happening-fast-enough, discouraged soul.

God shows Mommy how she is like me. He then says to her:

> Come to me, allow me to support your body as you rest in My arms, laying your head on My lap, and let Me show you that I've got you. Stay snuggled up to Me, and when it is time for your "feeding," by My movement, I will gently get you up and walk you to where your next "meal" is. But meantime, enjoy your place here—in My lap—letting Me lavish You in My love.

God's words are so comforting to Mommy. Anytime He gives Mommy new words that are different from His Word, her next step is to go to the Bible and to look up related scriptures. Here are three verses about Him leading her and being with her:

Be still, and know that I am God (Psalm 46:10, ESV).

And the peace of God, which surpasses all understanding, will guard your hearts and your minds in Christ Jesus (Philippians 4:7, ESV).

I will be with you. I will not leave you or forsake you. (Joshua 1:5, ESV).

Before we go further about stopping uncontrollable wailing, Mommy and I want to share that we know that there are sometimes when wailing is necessary. When grief or tragedy strikes, for example.

We're not talking about those times.

We're talking about the day-to-day issues that Mommy (and many other humans) get way too worked up about.

Instead, God is calling Mommy and other humans to:

- Be still.

- Trust.

- Cry out.

- Listen to His soothing response.

- Receive His love.

What About You?

Mommy and I invite you to receive this gift—to allow God to comfort you to help cease any of your unnecessary, uncontrollable wailing as you wait for Him.

God has good gifts for you, even if you can't see what those are yet.

If you are a fur parent or a parent of small humans, you likely understand that you can't always give precious family members what they want when they want it. Despite the protests, you may have to refrain from giving them what they desire to do what is best for them.

It's the same way for God…You may never understand why He's withholding something from you this side of Heaven…He may reveal the reason—eventually—or not. Either way, Mommy and I promise you: He is there to comfort you.

Next time you are stewing about something that you know in your gut isn't truly one of life's tragedies, just ask God for His comfort and see if your uncontrollable wailing ceases.

Meow for now,

Clive

I trust my Mommy, and I don't mind the scent of her toes!

43
SCENTS AND TRUST

One day, I heard my mommy praying, "Lord, please help me TRUST you."

Then she glanced over at me, and I saw that she looked overwhelmed. I looked back at her for a second, and I returned to what I was doing—rubbing my head on Daddy's shoes.

Then, all of a sudden, Mommy started to laugh out loud! I looked at her again as if to ask, "What's so funny?" She began to tell me about a rhyme that she learned when she was a little girl.

"Trick or treat. Smell my feet. Give me something good to eat..."

Mommy told me humans don't like to smell feet because they think they smell gross…That's what makes this rhyme funny to human children. Humans don't believe feet smells are enticing, nor do they want to eat feet-related snacks!

But we felines love feet smells—especially those from our owners. I know what you are thinking, *Eww, gross!* But this propensity for smells that repel you humans actually entice us to you. As you can see in the photo to the left, I smell mommy's feet and let her rest her feet on me. And I frequently lay on Daddy's shoes, rubbing my head on them. Rubbing up on shoes is one way we mark our territory. We are saying to humans—about their shoes, "I belong here, there, and wherever you are—and no other animals do."

As Mommy continued to giggle, I went over to her and jumped up in her lap, settling once again on my favorite blanket. I nestled my head into my journal where Mommy is putting pen to paper with my thoughts right now. I realized that I didn't have to settle for a left-over smell when I have access to—and am invited to—experience complete snuggling, full-body rubs, and soothing head scratches.

That's what it is like for humans with Big Daddy. Humans are invited to experience more than His left-over scents.

Thinking about this concept about Big Daddy's scents led Mommy to wonder: *What does God smell like?* She said her first thoughts were honeysuckle, which she fell in love with after she moved to Tennessee, and spring rain.

She then pondered, *What would be happening if a room had a fragrance that smelled like God?* She paused for a minute and answered her own thoughts. *People could be crying out for change with a fervent, heart-felt prayer…People could be boldly reading a passage of Scripture…Or people could be singing with all their hearts during a worship experience.*

She went on to think that Big Daddy doesn't just want some humans to experience His scent just for the benefit of themselves. Instead, Big Daddy wants humans to BE the fragrance of Christ! He wants them to exude childlike fun with a spring in their step to represent His fun! Big Daddy doesn't want humans to be territorial like we cats, who want to keep other cats away from their owner(s). On the contrary, Big Daddy wants humans to share Him as they interact with others.

When others see God-like qualities, like gentleness, joy, trust, and peace in some humans, it's as if His scent is spreading through the room. When these other people smell the amazing fragrance of Big Daddy, they will want to know more about who Big Daddy is for themselves.

The humans who have been influenced by others with His fragrance will start to run toward Him, whether for the first time or the hundredth time. As they begin to run, Big Daddy will throw his arms wide open and invite this new group of people smelling His scent to jump into His lap.

Then, just like Mommy cares for me, Big Daddy will caress these humans who have just turned to Him with His loving care. He will then settle their spirits as He speaks to them with love, just like Mommy does to me.

"Welcome home," Big Daddy will say. "Want to stay and play?"

Humans will continue to be drawn to His invitation and feel at ease in an animal-like posture as they feel His peace. As new humans continue to be with Big Daddy, they will experience the TRUST that comes from being loved completely as they have always longed to be. Then, Big Daddy will create a fragrance of love and peace in these new people that will in turn rub off on others who they interact with.

And so, Big Daddy's fragrance moves from one person to the next…and the next…

His attractive scent never fades, and it never excludes. What a picture of infectious love, ongoing care, and abundance for all!

What About You?

Is there a person you trust that you love to be around? Does he or she always make you feel welcome and seem to care about you?

Can you remember a time when you walked into a room or a person's home, and you just felt comfortable? If so, take a minute to consider what made the environment feel so soothing. Is there something that you could replicate easily in your home? Perhaps burn a candle, use an essential oil diffuser, or bake a fantastic smelling, no-fuss desert to add a pleasant aroma.

What "scents" in the abstract sense do you think you give off when you walk by or interact with someone?

Mommy says that a smile or a nod can brighten another human's day. She also says that the more she trusts Big Daddy, the easier it is to NOT focus on her own stress. Then, she can let His "fragrance" flow into her and out toward others. She says she learned this from Big Daddy's book by reading the following verse…

> Through our yielded lives he spreads the fragrance of the knowledge
> of God everywhere we go (2 Corinthians 2:14, TPT).

Well now that you are thinking about good scents and how you can leave one, it's time for me to take my own advice. I like to work on my own scent—with a bath! I'm uber clean as I've mentioned, and I want my humans to know it. So, I'll have to get their attention first so they can see me in all my bathing glory…

Meow for now,

Clive

Honoring my favorite veteran on a daily basis as soon he gets home from work...he hasn't even taken his badge off yet, but I am comfortable!

44

HONORING VETERANS

In this musing, I take a break from the typical feline frolicking as I stand in solidarity with my daddy.

As he rose this morning—albeit a bit later than normal because he had the day off for Veteran's Day—he surprised both Mommy and me as he emotionally gripped an encased flag and his army men.

Daddy served proudly for eight years in the Army National Guard, ending his tour with the 475th MASH (an army hospital).

Daddy spoke of the ever-present conflict of being away from family that constantly grips each soldier's heart. He shared that he had hoped to parachute out of planes and to go on missions to get our enemies. His service, however, kept him stateside.

He was also remembering his own father, whose casket that flag had draped over a decade ago. Daddy loved his father, though at times, Daddy wished his father hadn't been so difficult. Daddy laughed as he remembered his father mowing the lawn in dress shoes and doing his best to dress up, even though his sense of fashion was sometimes questionable.

That man was my grandpa, and I never met him. Daddy says his daddy was honorably discharged from the BATTLE AXE REGIMENT of THE FIGHTING 69 INFANTRY DIVISION. He was, however, one of the fortunate soldiers from World War II, because he lived a full life before he died of natural causes at 88 years old.

Daddy was also praying and crying out for those whose families made the ultimate sacrifice for our country.

He lifted up those who are still in harm's way. He specifically thought of our dear friend, John, who serves today in the Navy overseas, with his wife and three children a world away.

Daddy asked for our merciful God to not only protect all U.S. soldiers today, but also he asked that their hearts would be protected from the addiction to mind-altering substances or pornography that is rampant among military servicemen.

Daddy was mourning the country he knew as a youth—and wondered where the old-fashioned moral standards he knew as a pastor's son growing up more than 20 years ago have gone. He wondered what our country will be like when his grandchildren become adults.

He wondered if he was asked to serve today, what ideals would he be fighting for? Would he, if serving today, be able to express His love for Jesus Christ without being told he was offending someone or being asked to keep his faith separate from the front lines?

Difficult questions indeed—and ones that our veterans and active military face each day. I am just a cat, but I empathize with my daddy. So, I stare in awe of this flag and these army men—and we—in this family—offer our prayers and deep-felt gratitude.

After all, veterans and people in the military do what Jesus did—they are willing to lay down their lives for others. In fact, Jesus affirms this sacrificial action with his words when He said:

> "No one has greater love [nor stronger commitment] than to lay down his own life for his friends" (John 15:13, AMP).

What About You?

Is there someone you know who is in the military currently or a veteran? Have you talked to them about their experience or shown an interest in his or her service? Would you feel comfortable thanking those you know—or even those you don't know—for their service? If that feels genuine to you, Daddy encourages you to share that sentiment with a service member. It means so much to him when people thank Him in person or at events when veterans are asked to stand.

Could you attend a veteran's parade and wave? Could you give a donation to a veteran's charity? Or perhaps you could lend your prayers. Daddy says any of these actions are appreciated, and I believe him…He's SO smart! I LOVE MY DADDY!

Meow for now,

Clive

Honoring my grandpa's flag, reflecting in solidarity with Daddy's miniature army guy.

With my pen in hand...pondering what I'm grateful for, about to write in my favorite journal.

45

10 Things
I'm Grateful For

At this time of year, Mommy and Daddy are talking about thankfulness. They intentionally remember the blessings and experiences they have shared over the past year, and they write those things down. Since I want to be like them, I am doing the same. You might find this list somewhat predictable, but Mommy tells me it's okay to repeat our thanks as often as possible. So here's what I'm thankful for—at Thanksgiving and always.

1. **Mommy and Daddy.** They love me, feed me, pet me, hold me, let me be the center of attention, and they put up with all my crazy (but cute) antics. They let me sleep as they write, and they take lots of pictures of me to help me fulfill my dream of sharing my cuteness and insights with the world.

2. **Laps and chests.** My favorite place to lie is on a lap if my people are sitting up. If they are lying down, I get on top of their chests. I purr and snort and carry on. All my people have to do is pet me. And, if you come over to our house and if you stay for an hour or more, I will most likely jump on your lap too. My Gigi (grandma) visits us for longer periods of time, and I get on top of her chest as she rests, too!

3. **Morning couch time.** As I've said, this special time is when Mommy, Daddy, and I read the Bible and pray. Mommy and Daddy sip hot beverages as they ask Big Daddy (God) for guidance about work and life issues. They also lift up family members and friends. I cross my hands and pray right along with them, as I sit patiently. Mommy and Daddy

trust Big Daddy to direct them every day, and He faithfully shows them His priorities!

4. **My foodie!** I know my love for foodie may be obvious by my 23-pound, burly feline physique. But, just in case you have been skimming these pages or you can't tell how much I eat from the pictures, let me tell you once again—I LOVE MY FOODIE! Even though my humans ration my foodie and have me on a weight-loss formula, I still love to eat!

5. **My humans' foodie: protein shakes.** As I've also shared, my humans have been consuming these drinkable delights for years for either weight loss or health. I meow for them every morning like CRAZY! I know that when my humans move around after couch time that my tastes of their shakes are coming!

6. **Hair ties.** As I have shared, these little round circles are better than any cat toy on the market, hands down. I love to get my paws in them and throw them down the hall. It's my ongoing source of simple entertainment that never gets old.

7. **Daddy's shoes.** I've said it dozens of times, but I love everything about my Daddy! He is kind and patient, yet macho and manly. I want to be just like him! When Daddy is not at home, I like to lay on his shoes, just to remember his scent. Sometimes, I even lick his shoes. Don't be grossed out—it's what cats do.

8. **"Sandwiches." As I've also told you before, a "sandwich" is a term that I coined for my hugs with my humans.** In one of our "sandwiches," Mommy uses me as a pillow. At first, I thought I wouldn't like it, but I was surprised. I would just purr for a long time. Then, when my humans first get home from going out, and just before they put me to bed each night, Daddy usually picks me up, and they hug with me in the middle. Other than morning couch time, a "parent sandwich" is my absolute favorite thing. I purr-snort in delight every time I receive one.

9. **My "box" and the bathroom.** I love my "box" to be clean. My "box" gets much use because I eat so much. But I don't only love my "box," I love my humans' "box"—the bathroom—as well. I love it so much that, as I've said, I bust the door open to get in there whenever my humans are in there. I love to sit on their feet in front of the toilet. I also love to hang out with them when they get ready. You may recall that I put my paws up on the sink and stand on the toilet just to be with them. They try not to let me drink toilet water or water after they have showered from the tub,

but sometimes I sneak some anyway. I'll say it again: Don't be grossed out—it's what cats do!

10. **A home.** I have lived in all kinds of homes. As a younger cat, I lived in a house with three ladies. Then my mommy and daddy got married, and I moved into an apartment. I loved that I could see both of them most of the time. Then we moved into a small, freestanding farm-cottage-style house that was about the same size as our apartment. Mommy and Daddy and I were still cozy, but I had a prettier view of a hill and trees. Next, we got a second bedroom in a duplex in a subdivision. I had a street-level view and two neighbor dogs, who I could hear bark occasionally. More recently, we moved into the home we live in now, which is bigger with even more trees than our farm cottage. I love looking at the birds and the trees in our yard! On the other side of our house, I look out at a quiet street, where I watch our neighbors and dogs walk. I have to make sure the canines don't' come in! In this house, we have enough space to spread out if we need to. And Mommy and Daddy do now spread out when they work from home. But at night, we enjoy time together either at the table, in front of the fire, on the couch, or in the bedroom.

Phew! I hit 10, that's enough. Time for my cat nap!

What About You?

Could you easily list 10 things you are grateful for? If not, how about three to five things? Family? Friends? Health? Accomplishments? Foodie?

Mommy tells me (and the other writers she coaches) to start every writing session with gratitude to God. She says all humans have either blessings from the good parts in life or lessons uncovered from enduring tough situations.

> Be cheerful no matter what; pray all the time; thank God no matter what happens. This is the way God wants you who belong to Christ Jesus to live (1 Thessalonians 5:18, MSG).

Mommy also says that humans learn to love each other more as they share the not-so-great parts too. Perhaps your struggle will transform to a testimony someday…

Meow for now,

Clive

In my favorite Christmas bag that
is so meaningful to Mommy...

46
THE MOST WONDERFUL TIME OF THE YEAR—AND THE GIFT IN THE BAG

A h, Christmastime! Time for Christmas cheer!

Mommy and Daddy are extra happy and festive, and that means they are prone to give me extra treats. Daddy likes to not only have creamer in the morning, but he also likes to have just a smidgeon of eggnog each evening for a week or two during December. And he loves me so much that he gives me a taste every time he has something creamy!

I LOVE MY CHRISTMAS TREATS!!
I also love the whole Christmas decoration thing. When Mommy and Daddy get out all the decorations, bags and boxes abound for me to jump into while the decorations are either being put up or taken down.

I especially love the bag in the picture to the left because it is just my size. My mommy says that this is one

I play in the tissue that matches my eyes!

185

of her favorite pictures of me. I can see why! I sit in this bag under the tree as long as she will let me!

She also loves this picture because she loves the contents of what comes out of this bag each year. She lovingly reaches into this bag and unwraps a Christmas village of Liberty Falls, Colorado, circa 1878, that belonged to Great Grandma Faith and Great Grandpa Leo. She and Daddy carefully look at the map of the arrangement of the town to place each item precisely where it goes in their mini village set up.

As Mommy places each building on a special table near the Christmas tree, she remembers how much she loves and misses her grandparents, who are in Heaven now. As she talks about them, I am also grateful for Mommy's grandparents because they are the ones who first exposed Mommy to cats.

As Mommy was growing up, she went to her grandma's house in Meade, Kansas, where she played with a new litter of kittens each summer. Great Grandma Faith would bring some of the babies inside for her grandkids to play with. The grandkids gave each kitten a name, and eventually, Mommy got to take one home.

Mommy loved kittens so much that as soon as she could read, she subscribed to Cat Fancy magazine, which taught her how to be an even better cat Mommy. Who knows, maybe she can write an article for that magazine someday!

So, at Christmastime, I not only love playing in the bag, but I love to listen to Mommy as she reminisces about what this bag represents. The tree looks so beautiful that I gaze up at it and eventually fall sleep under it. When I am under the tree, I like to think I am reminding my humans that getting to adopt me was one of the best presents they ever received. I know they agree.

As beautiful as the tree is all lit up, when we have "couchtime with Christ" each morning, Mommy and Daddy remind me about the real reason for Christmas. They tell me once again that Big Daddy sent the best present of all time—His Son Jesus—to humans at Christmastime. As Christmas approaches, Mommy and Daddy read about the birth of Jesus in the various Gospels.

They also talk about how Jesus, the Light of the World, brought the light of hope, peace, and joy to the difficulties and darkness of life on Earth. Not only did Jesus bring this light, but His light living in humans who believe in Him enables humans to carry this light.

As Jesus says:
> "I am the light of the world. Whoever follows me will not walk in darkness, but will have the light of life" (John 8:12, ESV).

> "You are the light of the world. A city set on a hill cannot be hidden. Nor do people light a lamp and put it under a basket, but on a stand, and it gives light to all in the house. In the same way, let your light shine before others, so that they may see your good works and give glory to your Father who is in heaven" (Matthew 5:14–16, ESV).

Not only does Jesus bring light to this world, but He enables humans to be reunited with loved ones in Heaven. People are only able to go to Heaven because Jesus came to repair the breach between mankind, who chose evil in the Garden of Eden, and a perfect, Holy God. Mommy, who misses her grandparents every day, is excited to see them again in Heaven.

So, as you likely know, at Christmas, humans celebrate the gift of the birth of Jesus. They celebrate receiving His hope, joy, and peace, despite the difficulties of life. They rejoice over the promise of living in Heaven after this life is over. In Heaven, humans will not only have the joy of being reunited with loved ones, but also, they will live forever in Heaven without darkness as they gaze and interact with the Light of the World.

What an amazing gift!

Mommy not only celebrates the original gift of Jesus at Christmas time, but she also asks Jesus what fresh insight He wants to give her as a gift. Mommy says that this year, she is receiving a fresh gift of peace. As she thinks about the Christmas village, she considers that people in 1878 struggled, waiting for God to provide just as her grandparents did as children living through The Great Depression in the 1930s. Mommy and Daddy are blessed, but as she types these words, Daddy's income, which has been stable since they got married, is changing. Realizing how Big Daddy has met people's needs throughout the ages gives her comfort that He will meet their needs moving into the future as well.

And that is the gift her heart needs right now most of all.

That was pretty deep theological cat lesson. I know Daddy, a Bible school graduate, is proud of my sermon. Time for a cat nap, but first, I have to ask…

What About You?

Do you enjoy extra treats at Christmas? What are they?

Do your decorations remind you of other humans you love like my mommy's Christmas village reminds her of grandparents? Have you received the gift of peace on Earth and eternal life through Jesus? If so, what gift is He giving you today?

Maybe consider praising Him for any treats or new gifts you may have received recently before you take your next cat nap. ☺

Meow for now,

Clive

At peace loving my humans—doing what I was created to do!

47

THE PEACE IN DOING WHAT YOU ARE CREATED TO DO

Big Daddy created me as a loving cat. As I've said many times in this book now, I'm so grateful for my human daddy. That's why I'm fine telling you again. When you are really thankful for something, Mommy says that it's fine to talk about it every day. So I do.

Anyway, I love being in Daddy's arms. Maybe it's because I didn't get a human daddy until I was about five, when Daddy married my mommy. But I soon grew to love him so much because he is so good to me.

I love everything about snuggling my daddy. It gives me so much peace. So much peace that I can even fall asleep when Daddy rests his head on me. Before you other felines allow your humans to rest on you, remember that I am also a BIG cat hovering around 23 pounds. That means that I can easily support the weight of one of my human's heads. As I've also alluded to in other musings, I believe one of the reasons I was created by Big Daddy was to be one of my human's pillows. Therefore, it delights me when my daddy chooses to make me His pillow.

I am a cat with clear instincts. My thoughts usually don't get in the way of me carrying out that purpose. However, since humans have choices, I believe it can be harder for them to choose what to do than it is for me to choose my activities. Humans can feel pressured to do things that are the opposite of what they are created to do because of a need for money or because a certain activity is what society says they are supposed to do.

My humans, for example, both believed for many years that they needed to work for large companies to have stability. That idea is good in theory, except working for a large employer with structure, competition, and rules doesn't match the personality that Big Daddy gave either of my humans. My humans like freedom to set their own schedules, working and living at a flexible pace that they were created for. For a while, Big Daddy allowed them to choose work for larger companies, and they did learn some great skills along the way that are serving them well today.

However, in their "corporate careers," neither one of them had the peace that Big Daddy longs for them to have. Mommy and Daddy couldn't find that peace when they were trying to be somebody OTHER than who Big Daddy created them to be.

They didn't have the peace you see on my face in the picture of me being with Daddy. Mommy wasn't creating her own content that shares part of her story that might help others. Daddy wasn't delighting in creating wood products and art that decorate the homes or yards of other humans.

Even though I am a cat, I have felt some of this pressure. If I learned too much from cats in culture, I would have to learn to be aloof and to ignore my humans. I would have to have a "catitude" more often, and I would get myself into all kinds of mischief like my fellow felines do.

Mommy said she was done having cats before me. One of the cats she had was NOT NICE. He peed everywhere and broke glasses that were left on the counter by getting up there and knocking them off.

My point is that I won Mommy's heart, and when my previous owner was wanting to find someone else to care for me, she knew my mommy was the right person, and I would have been delighted had I gone to live with only her. As I've shared, when Daddy married Mommy, he made it possible for them to adopt me together. This action enabled me to expand my love to TWO amazing humans instead of one. And Big Daddy orchestrated circumstances that made that possible.

I know I was created to show my humans love and to inspire them to share my love for them with you. All three of us hope our journey has both inspired you and made you laugh along the way

What About You

If you don't know what you are created to do, Mommy and I encourage you to ask Big Daddy. His book says that:

> For we are his creative work, having been created in Christ Jesus for good works that God prepared beforehand so we can do them (Ephesians 2:10, NET).

If you know what you are created to do but don't have a way to do it, we suggest asking Big Daddy to make a way when there seems like there is no way.

Big Daddy has given my Mommy and Daddy peace, direction, and the means to carry out their passions, and we believe that He will do the same for you.

As I've said elsewhere, what do you have to lose if you ask Him? He might just change your life too!

Meow for now,

Clive

Humans, share these lessons with your felines, and they will live an enriched life—just like me! Ha! 🐱

48

9 LESSONS FOR YOUNGER CATS

I am an older cat now as I write. Because I have some life under my belt, I have some lessons to share with anyone who is interested. I could mostly share with other cats about how to be better behaved cats, since I behave so well—most of the time. As I have shared in this book, as long as my "box" isn't too dirty, I'm a good cat.

I think some of my kind would be willing to listen, and some of them wouldn't want to. Some of them might ask for help on some issues, but they may want me to mind my own business about other situations.

I do what I'm here to do regardless of what you think…I offer advice. I really don't care if you digest it or not. It's here for any human and cat who wants it.

Mommy tells a story about how she and Daddy went away for the weekend, when a book they had never heard of captured their hearts. They read the whole thing in a day.

I don't know if this book is like that. I really wrote it so Mommy could have fun and produce a book about a subject that wasn't quite as deep as her other books.

But since I'm here, I'm going to summarize the lessons I've learned for my fellow felines. You would do well to read this list to your cat. If you don't have a cat, adopt one and then share this list with your new pet ☺. Now back to the subject at hand—lessons for cats…

1. **Lesson One: If you are an indoor cat, don't try to go outside.**

- Why would I (or you) want to get away from secure food where you have to compete for it with other animals? Just remember what I always say: I LOVE MY FOODIE!

- I wouldn't want to get lost and be away from my humans—we would both be so sad!

2. **Lesson Two: Let your mommy and daddy snuggle you for a short amount of time any time they want to—and purr.**

- They are paying for the food, and I hope that you, like me, want to be respectful of those who are providing for you.

- They love you and want to snuggle you—otherwise, they wouldn't have a pet. So, LOVE THEM BACK!

- If you purr, they will not hold you for an indefinite period of time. Humans have things to do. If they do snuggle you for an extra-long time, perhaps they are sad and need the extra attention. What are you really doing besides sleeping and eating that you can't be with them for a little longer?

3. **Lesson Three: For the sake of fellow felines, be nice to visitors.**

- If you are nice to visitors, those people who don't have pets may decide to get a cat. They may realize how much easier we are than dogs, and after their current dog is no longer with them, they may decide to get a cat.

- Do not bite the visitors or be mad at them for getting in your space.

- Instead, either rub up against their legs, offer a gentle, cute "mrr" (which means thank you) or roll over and "play cute." They will likely be looking at you at that point, and they will start talking about how sweet you are.

- If all the people are sitting down (but not at a table to eat), this is the perfect time to get in your owner's lap and lay down.

- The other people will see this action as sweet, and then they will want a cat too—as long as cat hair doesn't make them sneeze too bad.

4. **Lesson Four: use your "box."**

    - Not using a litter box is one of the main reasons that might make your human want our kind to not live with them any longer. Most of you healthy felines can choose where you do business or go to the proverbial "loo." We know some humans have to make us go elsewhere because they are allergic to us, and they can't help that. My point is, just go in your "box"—even if it isn't as clean as you like.

    - I admit, even I sometimes tell my humans my "box" is too dirty by leaving my poop on the floor. They can clean the poop from the floor more easily than they can clean up pee. So, if you have carpet, NEVER pee on it. That might be grounds for immediate dismissal.

    - I know my humans love me, and if I have to, I leave one small poop ball on the floor to give them the message that they forgot to clean my "box." They just get busy sometimes and forget. A gentle reminder usually will suffice.

5. **Lesson Five: eat slow.**

    - Your stomach wasn't designed to gulp down food. Take time to chew your food and enjoy it. I don't have this skill mastered, so my parents had to put my food in a maze that makes me eat it slower. Otherwise, I eat fast and throw up. And then I am REALLY HUNGRY AND GRUMPY! And that combination isn't good for my humans or for me.

6. **Lesson Six: When all else fails, take a cat nap.**

    - If you are hungry, and there is no foodie, take a nap.

    - If you are thirsty, and there is no water, go to the toilet and get a drink. Then take a nap from the exertion.

    - If you want attention, and no one is around, take a cat nap.

    - If you can't catch the mouse, take a cat nap.

    - If you didn't get the bug, take a cat nap.

- If you are tired of playing with light because you never catch it, take a cat nap.

- Everything can be what you want it to be in your dreams. You are full. You are loved. You have whatever you want, and you are rested. After you rest, you are ready to follow all the other lessons I've given you thus far.

7. **Lesson Seven: Listen when or if your people read the book that Big Daddy (God) wrote.**

- Big Daddy's book says that "He gives us everything we need for life and for holy living" (2 Peter 1:3, NLV). I don't pretend to know everything about what that statement means. However, Mommy and Daddy, who learn from Big Daddy every day, say this statement often—and I trust my humans.

- I think part of my good behavior is because Big Daddy is pleased with how I obey my mommy and Daddy. The Bible says to obey your parents, so I do! I am a good cat!

8. **Lesson Eight: Reread all these lessons again and commit to implement them.**

- If the list seems long to you, try doing one each day instead of all at once. I would venture to guess you are like other cats I know. You have a short memory.

9. **Lesson Nine: If you try your best, and mess up, there is grace for you to try again.**

- You may have to read this list several times to get all these pointers down.

- That's okay. This list isn't going anywhere, and all of us felines AND OUR HUMANS get a new chance to live every day.

- Big Daddy's book tells humans to forgive each other, and because my humans see me as their kid, that grace and forgiveness extends to me too—even though, technically, I passed them in age since in cat years I am older than they are. Age doesn't necessarily make me—or humans—wiser. Only applying wisdom so that wisdom turns into action makes a difference.

What About You?

As you mature and grow, what lessons is Big Daddy revealing to you? What practical tips do you have to share? Wise humans, as they mature, realize the more they learn, the more there is to know. These humans become open to learn new methods that will refine their lives.

And if humans don't learn, or they aren't "open" to learn, that's okay too.

Some humans will appreciate your lessons, and some won't. Big Daddy is most pleased with you when you do what He says. He isn't disappointed in you when others don't see the value in your lessons. He always celebrates you! He also isn't disappointed in you if you fail. If you never did another thing for Him, He would still celebrate having you as a son or daughter!

So just let Him love on you as He continues (or begins) to mold and shape you for His glory!

Meow for now,

Clive

Finding my faith, with my foundation on God's Word!

49

FINDING FAITH ON YOUR OWN

I get up in my humans' lap for "couchtime with Christ"—a time when they would read the Bible and pray together. I really love hearing my parents talk and read—especially God's Word.

I'm a cat, and God didn't give me as much of a brain to make my own decisions, although I do have good instincts.

One of those instincts makes me lie on the Bible after my humans have read it. I can't digest it myself, but I do believe Big Daddy is somehow influencing me through it. I know I will go to kitty Heaven because I am a good cat. I believe that is enough for an animal. What's different about animals and humans is that Big Daddy gives humans free will. Humans can choose to deny Big Daddy and Jesus more easily than most animals can, because most animals don't have that kind of intellect.

I am different, though! I am special…

Before I go further, I have to address something. I know some of you doubt pets will be in Heaven. I encourage you to read, or reread, Genesis and Revelation. You will learn that animals were in the Garden of Eden, and that there is a white horse in Heaven. If those animals are there, I believe there will be pets in Heaven.

As long as you know and love my big brother, Jesus, you can be there with me someday. I can't wait to tell all those who don't think animals will be in Heaven how wrong they are. That may not seem like a nice thing to say. I have to let those comments out occasionally—I am still a cat, and I still have a "catitude" sometimes! Anyway, after I tell these humans, "I told you so," I will give them the biggest snuggle, and I will help welcome them to their new home in Heaven!

Okay, now that that matter is settled, let me get back to the point—finding your faith and your purpose. I was put on Earth to share lessons about God, my humans, and anything else I think about, as well as to inspire Mommy to share my musings with you!

One important lesson for humans is that your faith has to be your own. You can't use the faith of your parents or siblings or your pastor to get into Heaven. So how do you get to Heaven yourself? Some of you may know, but in case any of you don't know, allow me to share what I've heard with you.

1. First, you ask Jesus (God's Son) to be in relationship with you and confess your belief in Him—that He both is Lord and that He died to forgive you from sin.

2. Then Jesus' lovingkindness leads you to repentance, which means that you turn from any wrongdoing you know of (also known as sin).

3. You begin to see that the fact that Jesus died for you and shed His blood IS WHAT MAKES IT POSSIBLE FOR YOU TO BE IN RELATIONSHIP with God. You accept that payment as a free gift.

4. If you don't know Big Daddy, you may not know that He is holy. He tells humans to be Holy because He is holy. The problem is that humans can't be holy on their own. They can only be Holy by allowing the blood of Jesus to cover them with the perfect holiness of Jesus.

5. Because Jesus' blood is payment for all sin when humans believe in Him, that faith in Jesus makes it possible for humans to be with God.

6. Once humans accept Jesus' free gift of eternal life, they have a lasting, permanent relationship with God.

7. God is the best of the best—He is the only One who gave His Son who gave everything for someone else—and accomplished everything once and for all time. He also expects nothing in return!

I'm pretty amazing and loving, but I probably started loving my humans because they feed me, provide me shelter, and clean my "box."

God loves humans and animals because He is LOVE. Humans don't have to do anything to earn Big Daddy's LOVE. He created them simply to invite them to receive His love. He is DELIGHTED when humans love Him back, but He doesn't require it as a condition of His love. His gift of love is always waiting.

But all people who want to accept Him need to do so on their own. That's how finding faith on your own works. My mommy and daddy are passionate about people loving God because they want everyone to experience the love—and the healing and freedom—that they enjoy.

What About You?

If you have made your faith your own, we know you are experiencing greater peace than you knew was possible–even in the midst of this hard world.

If you don't know Jesus, are you ready to? Read through the seven points above, and if you believe—or even if you want to believe, but don't yet, ask Jesus to prove Himself to you.

Even those who have made it the mission of their lives to prove that Jesus wasn't God have not been successful proving that position. If you need more convincing about who Jesus is, read *The Case for Christ* by Lee Stoebel, a former atheist and an award-winning journalist, or watch the movie by the same name.

Mommy and Daddy and I are praying you have or will choose to be with us in Heaven! It's going to be an eternal party with all the FOODIE we want—and no more diseases and tears!

Meow for now,

Clive

Cooling myself to feel better...
being adaptable!

50
BE ADAPTABLE AND SMART...
TO THE VERY END

Well friends, I hope you have enjoyed the wisdom, tips, and humor I've shared. All good things must come to an end—and so must this book.

I want to encourage you to keep adapting and using your brain as long as you can—despite difficulties. I am sad to report that as I write I have a difficulty. My mommy and daddy didn't know it, but I started to have a problem with my tongue a few weeks ago.

I started leaving food in my bowl. Mommy and Daddy likely thought I was just getting a bit more finicky as I aged. Because I'm like my mommy, who often leaves the very end of food and drinks...she thought I was just leaving what she calls "the yucky part" in my bowl.

However, I began having trouble eating a few days ago, so Mommy and Daddy took me to the vet.

The vet said I might have dental issues, and he said I would need to get blood-work before they could sedate me to look at my mouth further. Meantime, he told Mommy and Daddy to get me Fancy Feast. Ooohh! I have always wanted that deliciousness, but Mommy and Daddy have been feeding me weight loss food instead.

Mommy and Daddy DID get me Fancy Feast, and I was able to eat it—it was SO Yummy!! Like I had always dreamt about! Praise Big Daddy!

But they only gave me a teaspoon at a time, and I was still hungry.

That's when I came up with a really cool trick, though, to make MORE food soft. I scooped up a dry kibble from my bowl and carried it to my water. I let it sit there for a while, and voila—more soft food!! I kind of snuck more food! I LOVE MY FOODIE!

Unfortunately, I was not feeling my best again a few days later. I'm having a biopsy tomorrow. The vet says there is a 50% chance the large growth in my mouth that they were able to see when they sedated me could be cancerous. We should get the test results in a week or so.

And if I do have cancer, Mommy and Daddy will probably have to make the tough decision to send me to live with Big Daddy in Heaven as soon as possible, or they will have to watch me until I can no longer eat and drink, when Big Daddy decides it's time for me to go.

There's still a chance that the ulcer on my tongue could clear up if it's not cancer. My humans are praying for that—and so am I. I don't really want to leave them. But I also know I've done my absolute best each day being a cat angel to my mommy and daddy.

And now that I've dictated all that I've wanted to share to Mommy, everything I was sent here to share is recorded.

That's the beauty of writing. It makes our insights live on after our lives on Earth are over.

Mommy doesn't know it, but preserving my memory and getting this book out is the tool Big Daddy will use to get her over her fear of marketing her writing. It might be my final cat angel assignment.

You see, she will want to share everything I have taught her with anyone who wants to listen.

She will no longer care who listens, who likes, or who buys. Nor will she equate it with her worth.

She will just share these words to honor me and to allow the gift of writing that Big Daddy has given her to get out into the world.

Who this book blesses and why it blesses them isn't the point—and that's not for me or Mommy to know. The point is that she, like me, will be doing her part, until Big Daddy takes her home and reunites us.

I hope we've inspired you to do your part too…

Meow for now!

Clive the Cat (aka Jack) Staples Lewis Pepoon

A special photo with my humans and me during a special week.

51

A SPECIAL WEEK

Boy did I enjoy finally being able to eat all the Fancy Feast I could get down!

Mommy, Daddy, and I decided to make the most of the week when we were awaiting my test results. Mommy and Daddy spent a bunch of time lying on the floor and giving me lots of snuggles because I didn't feel like jumping up on the

Mommy holding my paw, as we comfort each other.

couch or the bed. We also had many "family piles," which is when I lie on Daddy, and Mommy snuggles us, laying her head on him too. I gave them my best purrs. I was doing my best to enjoy every second of being with them.

On Friday, I started to have greater pain. I hid and resisted being picked up, which is completely unlike me. Mommy and Daddy found me and took me back to the vet before the clinic closed for the weekend to see if they could help ease my pain.

It was a special weekend at our house, as Mommy was turning 50 in less than a week, and the first local celebration with friends was scheduled over the weekend. Mommy and Daddy had gone to Kansas City, where Mommy grew up, to celebrate with family earlier this month.

I was determined that I wasn't going to let my sickness ruin Mommy's celebration! Mommy put on a 50th crown and a sash, and both Daddy and her friends who came for dinner told her she looked beautiful.

These friends were newer friends who I hadn't met before. Like I always do, I got to show Mommy and Daddy's friends how uber cute I am. I did my best tricks of rubbing up against their legs as well as plopping on the floor and "playing cute." And then I did the best trick: Sitting up in a chair so they could see my tummy. Knowing I had been sick, these newer friends were so glad they got to meet me.

Aunt Carole, my first human came to visit! I still love her!

After dinner, Mommy and Daddy and their friends were going to an old-time country place in our small-ish town an hour west of Nashville, Tennessee. More of Mommy's friends were going to meet the group out. Daddy had prepared to sing "Dixieland Delight" to her at the local old time country music place, and Mommy planned to line dance some too. I was so happy that Mommy was going out to have a good time on this special milestone. I love her so much! I normally don't like it when they have to leave, but since I was needing to rest anyway, I was okay that they were going out this time.

I had a bad reaction to the steroid, which caused my breathing to be even more labored than it previously was. Initially when Mommy and Daddy found me after they got home after midnight that evening, they were scared that our time together was coming to an end. They laid down next to me, wondering if they should take me to the animal ER. After research and prayer, they decided to let the acute effects of the shot wear off. Thankfully, by the next morning, I was doing much better.

Aunt Carole (my first human) came over to see me the next day on Sunday. I let her hold me, and she took this wonderful picture of my Mommy, Daddy, and me. She had also been the one who'd taken my baby picture you saw at the beginning of the book.

Aunt Carole, Mommy, and I reminisced about me being little. Aunt Carole mentioned what a blessing it was for her to give me to her friend—my current Mommy. Aunt Carole had also come to take care of me when Mommy and Daddy were out of town. I never forgot my Aunt Carole, and I was so thankful that she came to see me.

Daddy and I spending some precious moments together.

Mommy, Daddy, and I continued to spend extra time together for the next few days. I also got to keep eating Fancy Feast—I LOVE MY FANCY FEAST! Mommy and Daddy let me to drink out of a dripping bathtub faucet, which they previously wouldn't keep on for me. With my sore tongue, however, it was easier on me to turn my head sideways and close my mouth quickly rather than lapping water up from a bowl. So, they let me drink from the bathtub.

I was determined to be well for Mommy's actual birthday, which fell on a Thursday. She went for a walk that morning and saw a rainbow, a special sign from Big Daddy that He was with her on the start of her new decade.

Mommy could see that I was okay, so she felt comfortable leaving for the afternoon and evening so she could go meet her friends at LifeFest, a Christian concert with numerous bands playing that was being held at Johnny Cash's old farm, minutes from our house. Mommy was so excited that this special event happened to fall on her birthday!

I know being with her friends and the music about Big Daddy ministered to her heart that night—and I got to give her the gift of not worrying about me.

The next morning, Mommy, Daddy, and I got the call from the vet with the news we didn't want.

I learned that I have the most aggressive form of cancer in my mouth, and there is nothing the vet can do to help. The vet says that I won't be able to eat or drink for very much longer. In fact, I am beginning to have an even harder time eating as I write.

Despite the news, I'm so thankful we have had this special week together. I'm so thankful that I have had a wonderful life with wonderful humans, and that I have helped move Mommy forward toward her purpose. And I'm thankful for each of you, my readers, for reading about my life.

Hopefully my antics have made you laugh, and hopefully thinking about the questions I asked you has helped you move forward to serving your purpose too.

Tomorrow is never promised, so my parting words to you are as follows:

Figure out and do what Big Daddy means for you to do each day, seeing your purpose as a gift. Instead of having a "catitude," live each day with the humor and love I have passed on to my humans—and hopefully to you.

Meow for now—until eternity,

Clive Staples Lewis Pepoon, aka Clive/Jack the Cat

EPILOGUE PART 1: A CONFIRMING VISION

I, Loral, was at a special gathering for women, which happened the day after my birthday. The speaker and host encouraged us to spend some time in the presence of the Lord.

As I closed my eyes, I could see myself sitting at Jesus' feet. Simultaneously, I was petting Jack's head (and holding his paw). Jesus was looking down at me, and He was so beautiful. He called Jack to look up, just as he always had. He put His hand out and invited him to touch His hand with his paw.

When Jesus held out His hand, Jack jumped up into His lap. After Jack was settled in Jesus' lap, I felt Jesus' power and freedom, which originated from His heart, go through Jack, down Jesus' legs, and into me so I could confidently stand up and move forward in complete freedom.

I felt fear release, and I finally felt ready to complete and widely share my drafted books.

Thank You God for this vision. I will miss my sweet fur baby, but I'm so grateful that You will go with me, and that Jack's (Clive's) legacy will live on!

EPILOGUE PART 2: IN APPRECIATION CLIVE'S DADDY—THE CLOSER

Without Clive's/Jack's daddy, Seth, this book would not exist. So, not only is Seth "The Closer" with Jack, as I'll explain, but he was also the catalyst. As I've shared before, I would not have been able to adopt Jack from his former owner if Seth hadn't asked me to marry him. He even said that we could adopt Jack when he proposed to me!

I also would not have had the freedom to write during the day and observe so much about Jack, turning his actions into the persona of Clive if Seth had not provided this freelance lifestyle for me so that I didn't have to have a full-time job outside the home. Seth's stability enabled me to pursue my dreams of writing part time and to start an editorial business to bring in our "fun money."

I have called Seth "The Closer" for quite some time. He does the tough jobs that I just don't love. Seth does these things out of love for me. He has always cleaned Jack's box because the smell of the litter grosses me out. He scrubs the pans with stuck-on gunk because they are cast iron and heavy. He fixes the cars, the plumbing, electrical issues, and so much more.

I'm so grateful for my sweet Seth...and that he served as "The Closer" for Jack.

As Clive said in his last musing (written on the day after my 50th birthday, just after we got the call that Jack had cancer), we noticed he wasn't able to eat or drink. We called the vet back and made the most difficult appointment at the end of the day. Between that call and the appointment, God confirmed in the vision I shared that it was time for Jack to go home to be with Him in Heaven.

When we got to the appointment at the vet, we stretched Jack across our laps as the vet gave Jack his first shot. Jack laid on the spot—across both of our laps—that had provided him so much comfort throughout his life. The vet said that lying on our laps would be his last memory. As Jack's eyes closed, I picked him up and kissed him. I then handed my beloved Jack to my Closer.

The vet had explained that the second euthanasia shot makes an animal's heart stop, which can be a bit more jarring to watch. I didn't want to be there for that part of the process. Although it wasn't required for one of us to be there, my Closer stayed.

In addition to staying until the very end of Jack's life on Earth, my Closer also wanted Jack to be buried on our property. Because it was raining, Seth bought a large white decorative tent, set it over the burial site, and dug. He also made a special handmade wooden box to lay Jack in.

My Closer took Jack's body from the vet's office, wrapped him in a blanket, and put him in his special box. But my Closer didn't stop there.

He then made a lovely memorial with a rock garden and a precious statue near our wooden swing, where we often sit in our yard. Now we can see and remember Jack anytime we go outside.

This gift—both the painful act of having to move Jack from the vet to his permanent resting home and the making of Jack's memorial—is one of the most special gifts I have ever received.

So, my deepest appreciation goes to my sweet Seth.

Seth also remembers with me, talking about the memories of Jack as they come up, and we shed tears.

We reinvented the "family pile"—there is no Jack on Seth's chest—only my arms lie there now. There is no "meat" in the "parent sandwich", as we aren't hugging Jack in the middle of us. There is no mamma or pappa "smash" on the bed, as there is no Jack lying on the bed for us to side snuggle.

But after each memory, we praise God for giving us such a special animal. And my Closer helps me shift the conversation from grief to gratitude to God, and we move on with our day.

Thank you, my sweet Seth. One day our home and our hearts will open to a new feline. But there will never be another Jack.

All my love to you both.

Loral

Loral

I'm in one of Heaven's many libraries, and I found the many books that you will write, Mommy!
Keep going! I love you!

ABOUT THE AUTHOR

Loral Pepoon is an inspirational author who sees and writes about God's handiwork in His creation and in animals. She loves adventures with her husband, Seth, on hiking trails and at the beach, shared at hiking-withyourhoney.com.

She also writes the transformative power of God in her life and how He has empowered her to equip others in her sphere of influence. Her two drafted books about her own life are expected to be published either later in 2023 or in 2024.

Loral's personal writings have been published in anthologies *From Tears to Triumph* and *360 Degrees of Grief*. Loral is also blessed to be a contributing writer and editor for *Our Story Magazine*, where she writes about inspiring other writers.

Loral also empowers authors as an editor, publisher, teacher, and writing coach. She periodically offers online writing courses and writing retreats. Loral has edited more than 100 books since 2015 through her editorial firm, Cowriterpro (cowriterpro.com). To provide excellent design and formatting for her authors regardless of their platform sizes, Loral acquired Selah Press Publishing (selah-press.com) in 2020.

Loral draws on more than 20 years of full-time experience leading writers and graphic designers as a managing editor, creative director, and marketing manager at Moody Global Ministries, Loyola University Chicago, and Morningstar, Inc. Loral earned a master's degree in journalism and a bachelor's degree in European Studies with minors in French and German.

When Loral is not with her husband or helping authors, you may find her using one of her other passions, which include serving Christ on an inner healing team, facilitating various spiritual small groups, and praying with others in church services, in organized prayer meetings, or via phone or via Zoom or other video chat software.

Loral's greatest joy after being a daughter of the King and wife to Seth is being a grafted-in nana to four adorable grandchildren and a bonus mom to two amazing adult daughters and their husbands.

To learn more about Loral, visit loralpepoon.com. There, you can also subscribe to her enewsletter to get Loral's updates delivered to your email box, which will have more about Clive and his animal friends, exploring in nature, God stories, and anything else she might want to write about.

Loral also invites you to interact with her using one of the following methods:

Facebook: loralpepoonofficial

Instagram: @loralpepoon

Email: loral@loralpepoon.com

Clive Staples Lewis Pepoon (Jack), Sr. Check out 10 adorable videos of Clive on the Website clivethecat.com (click on videos) or visit the YouTube channel @clivethecat.

What Clive Sr. started will continue on with the next feline generation with the addition of Clive Jr., who is expected to join our family in the summer months of 2023. We would love for you to follow the journey! We will post updates @coolclivethecat on Instagram.

ACKNOWLEDGMENTS

A work as significant as a book is a result of a lifetime of blessings from others. I can only call out a portion of the people who have influenced me.

Thank you to all those who influenced my gift of writing early on. To my brother, sister, and childhood friends, thank you for giving me early material to write in childhood diaries and letters. To Elizabeth Bennett, who I got to have numerous reading slumber parties with, thank you, because at the heart of every author is a reader, and without you, I don't know if I would have begun reading for fun.

To Miss Portman, my amazing third grade teacher, thank you for being the first to awaken the love of writing my own stories. Thank you to all my English and foreign language teachers and professors at The Barstow School and at the University of Tulsa for instilling in me a love of language and composition. Thank you to my journalism professors at University of Kansas who, during my master's degree program, taught me how to edit.

Thank you to all my bosses who led and mentored me during my nearly 20-year corporate career. I'm especially grateful to Mary Nowesnick, whose red pen sharpened my skills and whose trust in me gave me the confidence to become the leader of a creative team when that opportunity presented itself.

Thank you to Carole Palser—first for opening your home to me, which paved a way for me to move to my dream location—and for giving me a chance to meet and fall in love with precious Jack. Your kindness and influence extended when you entrusted Seth and me to become his adoptive parents.

Thank you to Lona Frazier for facilitating Heartprint Writers' group for 10 years (at the time of this writing). You not only provided a group that inspired me to write my own books, but a connection in that group made it possible for me to stay in Tennessee so that I could meet Seth.

That connection was Kayla Fioravanti. Thank you Kayla for entrusting me with editing work, from articles to your memoir. Thank you for being the first to endorse my editing abilities in Tennessee, which started the word-of-mouth train that fuels an editorial business nearly 10 years later. Thank you for also encouraging me to participate in a couple Blog Challenges that brought the first bit of Clive's persona to life. Thank you for also offering Seth and me Selah Press Publishing when it was time for you to move in a different direction. Your mentorship, friendship, and trust have been wonderful gifts to me—and to Seth.

Thank you to those who have been with me in this lifelong learning pursuit of all things related to writing: the members of Heartprint, my abiding writing group, my writing challenge participants, my students in my online writing courses, my coaching clients, and my editing and publishing clients. A special thanks to my Hope Writers accountability group, whose members were coworkers with me three days a week as I expanded Clive's words from a blog to a book.

Thank you to Venessa Knizley, my editor, for editing this book with as much scrutiny as I would edit one of my client's books. It was good for me to have a taste of my own medicine, lol. Your input was amazing. Thank you for giving me peace of mind in knowing my family's antics made sense. Thank you to Jenni McCadams for my headshots that I have used to pieces. You are so talented!

Thank you to all the prayer warriors in various small groups I've been a part of and to all of my friends whose precious prayers have been the behind-the-scenes momentum that keeps me going. You were and are God's tools of encouragement, strength, and endurance. You all either influenced my obedience, lifted me out of the proverbial pit, or helped me turn around when I was going the wrong direction.

I'd like to especially thank Tammy Stone, who has prayed with me most weeks for the last 10 years. Your faithfulness and wisdom is a precious treasure to me. I love you, Tammy!

Friends, this book is the first of three manuscripts that I have already drafted, and with many other ideas for future works, I will rely on your prayers and encouragement for years to come!

Thanks again to my sweet Seth, for everything I've already mentioned in the book and in the appreciation section. Thank you most of all for your amazing, steadfast love, for abiding in Big Daddy with me, and for not allowing me to give up on myself during life's challenges. Beside loving Christ, being your wife is my absolute favorite job I've ever had. Being a grandparent because of you is a very close second. Co-parenting Jack with you for seven and a half years was an amazing experience, for which I'm eternally grateful. I look forward to opening our home to other animals or to whomever else God brings us.

Thank you, most of all, to Big Daddy (God), Big Brother (Jesus), and to the Holy Spirit for not only saving me but also for loving me unconditionally and turning my life around. Thank you also for equipping me to share Your precious gift of love given to me through this precious animal. Thank you for showing me "this is that," by giving me a dream that I would give birth to a cat a year before I met Jack. Although I didn't physically birth him, I am birthing his persona into the world now!

Thank you, God, for giving me the observation skills and a love for journaling that made this book possible. Thank you for the gift of imagination and creativity that enhanced our experience having Jack as a pet. I'm so grateful (most days) for the gift of writing.

I'm placing this nearly finished book into your hands!

I'm asking that you show me how to do my part to share this book with those who you would want to read it!

I love You, Lord, and I trust you for the rest of the journey!

NOTES

1. Flavia Medrut, "Famous Inspirational CS Lewis Quotes about Love, Life, Humility and God," Goalcast, https://www.goalcast.com/15-c-s-lewis-quotes/, accessed March 22, 2023.

2. "About C.S. Lewis," *C.S. Lewis. The Official Website of C.S. Lewis,* https://www.cslewis.com/us/about-cs-lewis/, accessed March 22, 2023.

3. "About C.S. Lewis," *C.S. Lewis. The Official Website of C.S. Lewis,* https://www.cslewis.com/us/about-cs-lewis/, accessed March 22, 2023.

4. "C.S. Lewis Quotes," *Goodreads,* https://www.goodreads.com/quotes/44447-the-great-thing-if-one-can-is-to-stop-regarding, accessed March 22, 2023.

NOTES

1. Flavia Medrut, "Famous Inspirational CS Lewis Quotes about Love, Life, Humility and God," Goalcast, https://www.goalcast.com/15-c-s-lewis-quotes/, accessed March 22, 2023.

2. "About C.S. Lewis," *C.S. Lewis. The Official Website of C.S. Lewis,* https://www.cslewis.com/us/about-cs-lewis/, accessed March 22, 2023.

3. "About C.S. Lewis," *C.S. Lewis. The Official Website of C.S. Lewis,* https://www.cslewis.com/us/about-cs-lewis/, accessed March 22, 2023.

4. "C.S. Lewis Quotes," *Goodreads,* https://www.goodreads.com/quotes/44447-the-great-thing-if-one-can-is-to-stop-regarding, accessed March 22, 2023.

which I'm eternally grateful. I look forward to opening our home to other animals or to whomever else God brings us.

Thank you, most of all, to Big Daddy (God), Big Brother (Jesus), and to the Holy Spirit for not only saving me but also for loving me unconditionally and turning my life around. Thank you also for equipping me to share Your precious gift of love given to me through this precious animal. Thank you for showing me "this is that," by giving me a dream that I would give birth to a cat a year before I met Jack. Although I didn't physically birth him, I am birthing his persona into the world now!

Thank you, God, for giving me the observation skills and a love for journaling that made this book possible. Thank you for the gift of imagination and creativity that enhanced our experience having Jack as a pet. I'm so grateful (most days) for the gift of writing.

I'm placing this nearly finished book into your hands!

I'm asking that you show me how to do my part to share this book with those who you would want to read it!

I love You, Lord, and I trust you for the rest of the journey!

Made in the USA
Columbia, SC
10 January 2024

29954915R10128